Your Palm –
Barometer of Health

Your Palm –
Barometer of Health

David Brandon-Jones and
Veronica Bennett

RIDER
London Melbourne Sydney Auckland Johannesburg

To all at Poplar Farm (Charlie and goats included) and to the Hancocks, without whose encouragement, support and hospitality this book would never have been written. To Alan, whose deft management helped us see it through. And to P.S. – G. who, with integrity and not without misgiving, provided the key to this Pandora's box. And to Lawrence Zaidman.

Rider and Company

An imprint of the Hutchinson Publishing Group

17–21 Conway Street, London W I P 6J D

Hutchinson Publishing Group (Australia) Pty Ltd
16–22 Church Street, Hawthorn, Melbourne, Victoria 3122

Hutchinson Group (N Z) Ltd
32–34 View Road, P O Box 40–086, Glenfield, Auckland 10

Hutchinson Group (S A) Pty Ltd
P O Box 337, Bergvlei 2012, South Africa

First published 1985
© David Brandon-Jones and Veronica Bennett
Set in Bembo

Printed and bound in Great Britain by Anchor Brendon Ltd,
Tiptree, Essex

ISBN 0 09 159081 7

Contents

Introduction

There are . . . two kinds of health, natural and artificial. Scientific medicine has given to man artificial health, and protection against most infectious diseases. It is a marvellous gift. But man is not content with health that is only lack of malady and depends on special diets, chemicals, endocrine products, vitamins, periodical medical examinations, and the expensive attention of hospitals, doctors, and nurses. He wants natural health, which comes from resistance to infectious and degenerative diseases, from equilibrium of the nervous system. He must be constructed so as to live without thinking about his health. Medicine will achieve its greatest triumph when it discovers the means of rendering the body and the mind naturally immune to diseases, fatigue and fear. In remaking modern human beings we must endeavour to give them the freedom and the happiness engendered by the perfect soundness of organic and mental activities.

Alexis Carrel, *Man the Unknown*[1]

Dermatoglyphics is the hidden science, the one nobody outside a small and rigidly exclusive group knows anything about. It is more esoteric than the most secret occult 'ology'; its closest relative is the branch of police forensic work dealing with finger-print patterns. Yet it is a science with a recorded history going back beyond the seventeenth century; an important report on the subject was presented to the Royal Society in 1684. Why, then, are so few aware of this fascinating science and the tremendous potential it holds for the future benefit of mankind?

It seems that the prejudice bedevilling the efforts of scientific hand analysts to gain acceptance and respectability also hinders the work of dermatoglyphicists. Fortune-tellers and charlatans are inextricably linked with the process of examining palms in the popular imagination. How strange that, all too often, the scientists themselves – who by tradition are expected to be open-minded – actually impede progress.

Their research projects become an end in themselves rather than benefitting mankind – a dead end, some might say.

As a scientific hand analyst with an interest in anything that might expand the frontiers of my knowledge, the basic concepts underlying the science of dermatoglyphics intrigued me and I determined to explore the subject in greater depth. When I tried to make sense of the available literature, however, I was forced to retire, temporarily defeated. A boggy morass of incomprehensible jargon confronted me, larded for light relief with figures, statistics, and algebraic equations. Getting to grips with the actual subject seemed impossible for the mere layman!

Spurred on, however, by a cutting from an American newspaper sent by a friend and headed 'Doctors Reading Palms to Diagnose and Predict Disease', (in Europe and in America), I persevered with my studies and some time later *Your Palm – Barometer of Health* was conceived and commissioned. The result effectively translates and, the authors hope, demystifies some of the work being carried out today in North and South America, India, Japan, Australia, Israel, Scandinavia, Germany, France, Portugal, and Great Britain. We have synthesized these findings with the most up-to-date thinking in scientific and psychological hand analysis.

If the promise inherent in dermatoglyphics is to be fulfilled, we have to stop thinking in terms of 'spare-part' surgery and organ transplants. The task of healing the sick is in grave danger of falling into the hands of profit-makers for whom a healthy population would be financially disastrous. The powers-that-be must be distracted from their obsessive belief that there is a mechanistic solution to every symptom. Why should a transplanted liver or kidney work if the environmental pollution or other conditions that caused the original organ to fail still exist?

An individual's palms, or soles, can be read not just with the aim of diagnosing existing conditions but also predicting future ones. In the years to come, by applying the science of dermatoglyphics to the ever-present world-wide problems of mental and physical diseases, it may be possible to win valuable time; time in which the causes can be found and the processes of degeneration reversed. Healthy human bodies incorporate every conceivable fail-safe system. They are programmed to repair themselves in spite of the damage inflicted on them. Once those repairs are completed, the tell-tale signs in hands and feet disappear.

Your Palm – Barometer of Health is no more than an introduction to dermatoglyphics. The science itself is wide open for expansion and new ideas; it's far too important to remain hidden. The book represents our attempt to place a figurative candle in the gloom and illumine the darkness.

Part One

The Theory: Why hand analysis works

1

Palmistry to Dermatoglyphics – a Potted History

Are we not part of the whole? And therefore being a part must we not reflect the whole? Even as the cells of our bodies are tiny parts of us, each cell being complete in itself, in its individual cellular sphere, is it not true that we are the tiny cells of a greater body? Shall we not find in ourselves the workings of those forces we seek to discover, and in the patterns of ourselves shall we not find the total pattern of all things?

Noel Jaquin, *The Hand Speaks*[2]

Mention the word palmistry to the vast majority of the general populace and you're likely to get one of two basic responses – especially if you happen to let drop that you know a little about it. Either a hand will be shoved under your nose, with a cry of delight, and an exclamation such as, 'Oh! A *palmist* – how marvellous! I *love* to have my fortune told. Tell me, am I going to be rich?' (or famous, or swept off her feet by that elusive tall, dark, handsome stranger), or – and the two kinds of response are almost evenly divided – both hands will be thrust into pockets, or otherwise hidden. The accompanying comment this time is usually along the lines of, 'I don't want to know what the future holds in store for me. I prefer just to let life take its course.'

Invariably, palmistry conjures up the image of a darkened booth at the seaside or fairground and a mysterious figure surrounded by exotic artefacts and tools of the trade. A crystal ball and lurid astrological symbols at strategic points are almost inevitable adjuncts for this kind of reader, and help to conjure up that goose-pimpling, spine-chilling, other worldly atmosphere that never seems to fail to pack 'em in. Especially if he, or much more commonly she, has dark hair, an olive complexion, and hoop earrings. In short, a gipsy look.

Unless you're one of a very small minority, then, it will come as a big surprise to learn that palmistry has a substantial, if chequered, historical background with roots in the far-distant past, and that it is only comparatively recently that its reputation as one of the natural sciences has been swamped by a tide of unthinking, unreasoning superstition and fear. A little knowledge in the wrong hands can be extremely dangerous, and charlatans and quacks the world over have done, and indeed continue to do, a disservice to those of us who know that palmistry can be an art, or a science – or a skilful blend of both.

Since the dawn of the Dark Ages in Europe, palmistry in the West has remained under a cloud, together with astrology, and other 'heretical' occult and esoteric beliefs. At times, particularly when all the ancient tomes filled with the accumulated wisdom of centuries were seized and burned, it seemed that palmistry's light would be extinguished completely. Luckily, just enough written literature on the subject survived to augment the verbal and more practical teaching that was forced to continue underground. Now there were two strands being spun, where before there had only been one. Objective hand analysis took a back seat and fortune-telling became the rage. Gipsies and their ilk battened on the gullibility and weakness of the all-too-often unwary public. Many believed the tales of gipsy curses – curses that would plague them if they failed to cross the itinerant's palm with the appropriate amount in silver coin.

By the seventeenth century, when the rationalist movement started to gain adherents, hand reading had disintegrated into little more than a parlour game at best, and, at worst, remained a vehicle for the dubious talents of seers, diviners and common fortune-tellers. There was no obvious incentive for an intelligent man with the ability to reason to investigate such tomfoolery and it's hardly surprising to learn that most rationalists dismissed the subject outright. There was no outward sign to show that there was a pearl of great price within this dingy-looking 'oyster'.

From the very earliest times the study of the hand has excited man's curiosity and stimulated his imagination. Into the pattern of the lines on his palm he has projected the course of his destiny. Even the scientific rationalism of the last century did not succeed in defeating this credulity.

And,

It is true, the significance of hand-features in the diagnosis of a few illnesses is recognized in modern medicine, but these exceptions only accentuate the general indifference of physicians to the information which a patient's hand may furnish.[3]

The second branch of palmistry, and the one that we're mainly concerned with in this book, was extremely fragile but at the same time tenacious. The 'new' scientific hand analysis owes its existence to the growth of the rationalist movement which taught its followers not to accept anything on face value, to mistrust the supernatural, and to develop a more practical, reasoned approach to life than had hitherto been customary. Needless to say, the divergence between the two approaches to reading hands was by no means a clear-cut one. There were (and for that matter, still are) self-styled scientists of the hand whose results owe more than a little to clairvoyance, or 'intuitive' perception than to science. Not necessarily a bad thing, of course, provided the true source of enlightenment is acknowledged!

A more systematic approach to this search for knowledge was apparent by the early seventeenth century. Men of single-minded determination were seeking out and slaughtering all the feeble sacred cows they could find. Many, for their heresy, were figuratively if not literally burned at the stake for their pains. William Harvey, for example, in spite of his professional standing was denigrated and vilified for daring to suggest that blood circulated in the system continuously, for this idea ran counter to all contemporary thinking.

An exciting, and, at the time, revolutionary development was the founding in 1665 of the Royal Society in London, following in the footsteps of a similar society in Rome, and followed by the French *Académie des Sciences* in 1666. These societies were designed to promote the advancement of science and gave their members a certain degree of protection against the scorn and closed minds of the establishment. Safety in numbers, perhaps! In 1684, one Nehemiah Grew (1641–1712), an English doctor, presented to the Royal Society a report on his findings concerning the patterns on the fingers and palms of men's hands. He described the pores, the skin ridges and the way they were arranged, illustrating the report with a drawing which reproduced the skin-ridge patterns with remarkable clarity (see Figure 1). A year later, in 1685, Bidloo's book on human anatomy appeared. This included a detailed drawing of a thumb together with a precise description of the patterning (see Figure 2). In 1686 Marcello Malpighi (1628–94), the Italian anatomist, commented briefly in one of his works on the skin ridges and their variability. There's little doubt that the invention in 1609 of the microscope by the Dutchman, Zacharias Janssen, went a long way towards

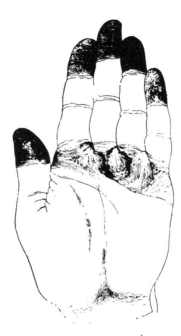

Figure 1   Skin-ridge patterns drawn by Nehemiah Grew, 1684

Figure 2   This drawing appeared in Bidloo's book – one of the earliest scientific records of dermatoglyphics, 1685

furthering the upsurge of interest in these curious patterns, their function and morphology. It was an invention that helped consolidate and advance the rationalist approach to science in general and medical research in particular. Malpighi summarizes the findings of all three men when he states,

The hand presents for examination, on its palmar surface, elevated ridges which course in diverse designs. On the terminal segments of the digits they are drawn into spirals; if examined microscopically they show the mouths of sweat glands along their middles.

For the most part, though, the two threads – divination from the lines and signs, or fortune-telling, and truly scientific hand analysis – seem to have remained tangled and confused right the way through into the nineteenth century. Not till then did the rational, scientific approach begin to gain recognition in its own right.

A strange medley of chiromancers parade through the sixteenth and seventeenth centuries – strange for other reasons than that they studied and practised this art. Most of them were what we might be tempted to call *typical* early Renaissance scholars: brilliant in many subjects, universal in comprehension, and above all filled with the spirit of enquiry and research . . .[4]

Swelling their numbers were such men as Cocles, Achillinus, Indagine, Tibertus Antiochus, Paracelsus, Goclenius and Robert Fludd. Though they made no great leaps away from the medieval traditions of the past, they laid the groundwork for those who would later do so.

Their main contribution to the art was that they gave it the grace of scholarship, refined the earlier teachings with sound argument, and deepened the interpretative content of special signs and symbols.[4]

Unfortunately, but understandably, the significance of this did not impinge on the consciousness of the masses who had, after all, been conditioned over many hundreds of years to see palmistry as a branch of knowledge that was magical, arcane, and only for the initiated. The sort of knowledge that had, until the age of rationalism, been the object of superstitious awe and dread in the West. But in India, China, and the East palmistry is, and has for centuries been, very much a part of daily life, with palmists and astrologers being accorded the same degree of respect that we used, till recently, to give the clergy.

During the eighteenth century, superficially at least, nothing of any great note happened in the world of palmistry.

Chiromancy had ceased to interest the scholars of the day: their way of thinking had changed a great deal, whereas chiromancy had changed scarcely at all. The art could simply not be fitted into the new intellectual and emotional need for a 'scientific method'.[4]

Anatomical works in general though were beginning to analyse and describe the peculiarities of the skin ridges, and to take note of the unique variations between them in different people. This seems to have been recognized as far back as 1691. It was in that year that 225 good men and true of the City of Londonderry appended finger and thumb prints to an official document by way of identification.

Meyer's book of anatomical illustrations published in 1788 includes a plate of carefully drawn fingerprints – a full set. He comments,

Although the arrangement of skin ridges is never duplicated in two persons, nevertheless the similarities are closer among some individuals. In others the differences are marked, yet in spite of their peculiarities of arrangement all have a certain likeness.

The nineteenth century saw a great upsurge of interest on all fronts into both natural and supernatural phenomena, with each investigatory body claiming an approach that was in full accord with scientific principles. Many of these investigators were, it appeared later, guilty of self-delusion and not in the least objective. It's hardly surprising that, from this point onwards, right up to the present day, the genuine scientist has done all he could to dissociate himself and his projects from what he still regards as the dangerous and incompetent meddling of the pseudo-scientist. Inevitably, though understandably, this has led to much valuable and significant work being ignored.

However, being a scientist isn't just the prerogative of one who has studied and qualified for the label of chemist, biologist, physicist, anthropologist or whatever. Paper qualifications may be highly regarded, even sought after. They certainly aren't essential. Anyone using scientific methods is a scientist, but he'll find it much more difficult to prove his points valid, for his qualified brothers will do their level best to trip him up, publicly if they can. The same applies to any scientist who dares to try and rock the boat with unconventional theories. Hippocrates, Paracelsus, William Harvey and Charles Darwin were all rebels in their day, and their beliefs ridiculed by the establishment till in due course those same beliefs became respectable and indisputable in their turn.

Science has rigorously ignored the study of the hand, regardless of the facts that occultism formed the basis of scientific discovery: that astronomy developed from astrology; that little more than three centuries ago chemistry was evolved from alchemy; and that it was through occultism that the path of thought was first opened which, reaching beyond the plane of immediate experience, led to the development of philosophy and psychology.[3]

From the early nineteenth century onwards, the schism between the two major opposing factions grew ever wider. It might be more accurate to say that these new 'scientists of the hand' felt it safest to ignore all that had gone before in the name of palmistry. Indeed, it wasn't till the twentieth century that more than a passing reference was made to the lines so beloved of, and basic to, the fortune-teller and his art. Attention was focused instead on the 'morphology of the palmar skin and . . . the arrangement of ridges and pores'.[5]

The work of Jan Purkinje was an important landmark in the history of scientific hand analysis. Dr Purkinje was a brilliant Czech doctor and researcher who had been working on a thesis about the human hand and eye in Prague. He subsequently won a professorship to Breslau University and published the thesis in 1823. He was the first to make a systematic classification of the various types of fingerprint pattern, and to suggest that they might have genetic and diagnostic importance (see Figure 3).

In 1833, Sir Charles Bell, anatomist and Fellow of the Edinburgh

Figure 3   Jan Purkinje's nine types of finger patterns, 1823. A, the transverse curves (plain arch); B, the central longitudinal stria (tented arch); C, the oblique stripe (loop, ulnar or radial); D, the oblique loop (loop, ulnar or radial); E, the almond (whorl); F, the spiral (whorl); G, the ellipse – elliptical whorl (whorl); H, the circle – circular whorl (whorl); I, the double whorl (composite, twin loop)

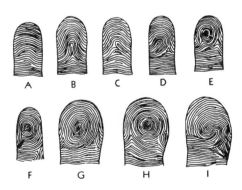

College of Surgeons, made his contribution to the growing literature on the study of the hand. His book was titled *The Hand – Its Mechanism and Vital Endowments as Evincing Design* (suitably ponderous and long-winded as befitted the era), and was one of the Bridgewater Treatises on the *Power, Wisdom and Goodness of God, as Manifested in the Creation*. The series as a whole was written more in the spirit of the early rationalism of the seventeenth and eighteenth centuries, but Bell's examination of the structural and functional adaptation of the human hand was concise and comprehensive.

Two Frenchmen, Captain Stanislas d'Arpentigny (1798–1865), and Adolph Desbarrolles (1801–86), have posthumously been credited with the honour of being the father of modern palmistry. Claims to the title have been made for each of the two men by their respective followers.

D'Arpentigny was an officer in the army of Napoleon. He was a critical observer of life and of people and when he retired from the army with honours at a reasonably early age, he resolved to devote himself to the study of palmistry in which he had been interested for many years. Having absorbed the history of his chosen subject from ancient times to date, he began to put it to the test by practising on those he came in contact with in daily life, people from all walks of life, throwing out the dross as he went. The highly refined and reduced results of his observations over the years formed the basis of modern chirognomy – the study of hand shape as it relates to character and personality.

His book, *La Chirognomie*, was a great success. The time was right for a fresh approach to palmistry and d'Arpentigny's new system for classifying hand types was scientific enough to be readily acceptable, yet highly readable, too. The 'system of seven' as it is called, has survived virtually intact to the present day despite several attempts to update and replace it, yet contemporary hands and minds:

have little in common with those described and illustrated 150 years ago. Although the System of Seven is widely used, even now, it seems rather unrealistic to divide the whole of humankind into a mere six categories. When it was devised, it was a great step forward for palmistry, but it is a system that seems to have outgrown its usefulness.[6]

Class distinction nowadays is less rigid, less clearly defined than it was in Captain d'Arpentigny's day, when the upper classes were careful to keep themselves aloof, 'cushioned and cocooned from the lower orders'. His description of the 'Elementary' hand type tells us quite a lot about d'Arpentigny's own background:

Such a character, inaccessible to reason from sheer want of originality of intellect to understand it, is sluggish, heavy and lazy as regards any occupation beyond its accustomed toil.

It is a type which, according to d'Arpentigny, 'belongs to the lowest grade of human intelligence'.

Desbarrolles, too, established his own original system. He took and wove together a strange fabric of Kabbalistic and astrological lore embroidered with elements of contemporary scientific thinking. His theories and 'planetary types' were to influence the course of intuitive palmistry for the next hundred years or so. These were set out in *Les Mystères de la Main* which was first published in 1859 and ran to more than twenty editions in his lifetime. In Fred Gettings' opinion,

except for the notable research done by many modern psychologists on the hand, it would be true to say that almost every teaching during the past hundred years has been but a refinement or simplification of the work of Desbarrolles and d'Arpentigny.[4]

This rather sweeping statement is certainly applicable to the kind of palm reading made popular by the two Frenchmen, but Fred Gettings is seemingly unaware of the highly significant research carried out by Herschel, Galton, Henry, and Vucetich towards the end of the nineteenth century – research which was to become the foundation for the science of *dermatoglyphics* as it exists today.

Although the public in general was apparently ready to look upon palmistry in a much more favourable light than had been fashionable for many a year – especially as its more popular proponents were quite obviously not gipsies – the orthodox scientific fraternity was not at all impressed by, nor even particularly interested in, the burgeoning fad for analyzing character and potential from the hand. Meanwhile, the dermatoglyphicists' progress towards understanding the purpose and relevance of the skin-ridge patterns in man went unnoticed and unremarked outside their own closed circle.

The German professor Carl Gustav Carus (1789–1869) was the first scientist to inquire into the psychological significance of bodily appearances. Both Carus and d'Arpentigny correlated their hand types with mentality and temperament but Carus had the sort of qualifications that were acceptable to and respected by the intelligentsia. At the age of twenty-six he became Professor at the Medical Surgery Academy of Dresden. Twelve years later, in 1827, he was appointed personal physician to the King of Saxony, and went on to become a member of the

Academies of St Petersburg, London, Philadelphia, Stockholm, Naples, and Florence. He presented his conclusions to the world in 1848, when *Uber Grund und Bedeutung der Verschiedenen Formen der Hand* was published. It did nothing to detract from his already formidable reputation although some of his views were well ahead of their time.

Sir Francis Galton (1822–1911) is often described as an anthropologist. Even in the broadest sense of the word it's a term altogether too rigid and inflexible to encompass the diversity of Galton's scientific activities. He possessed an inextinguishable desire to know all there was to know about the world around him, and to gain a measure of control over it by learning its laws.

His early scientific interests (geography, ethnology, and meteorology) were generated by travel, [but] a turning point in his interests occurred in the mid-1860s . . . thenceforth he engaged mainly in studies of biological variation, heredity, eugenics, statistical theory and practice, and fingerprints.[7]

Galton was also an inventor and developed the 'telotype'; a printing electric telegraph, a hand heliostat for sending light signals, and many other devices for use in his various research programmes.

Altogether he had published some 240 works, including fifteen books, the most important of which from our point of view was *Finger Prints*. This first appeared in 1892 and is still available, an acknowledged classic in the field of fingerprint identification and the study of the skin ridges generally. The book:

brought together and strengthened the evidences essential to the validation of fingerprints as means of personal identification . . . permanence of the fingerprint characteristics; uniqueness of an assemblage of ridge details; variability and classifiability of finger patterns . . . [and] reported on fundamental investigations: biological variation as manifested in fingerprints; inheritance of fingerprint traits; [and] variation among racial and constitutional groups.[7]

The work of Galton and his contemporaries made fingerprinting a respectable science. Notable among these contemporaries were Sir William Herschel who, as a Commissioner in India had, it seems, been using these 'finger marks' as a means of personal identification for many years, and Juan Vucetich, whose own system of classifying prints and using them for identification purposes was introduced in Argentina in 1891. Sir Edward Henry's system of identifying criminals from prints left at the scene of crime was adopted by Scotland Yard in 1901, and the first conviction using such evidence was made the following year.

The end of the nineteenth century was also marked by an upsurge of interest in palmistry generally. The Chirological Society was founded in April of 1889. It aimed to promote the study of the hand at a more scientific level, to itself instigate a programme of scientific research, to promote the study of the palm, and to protect the public from unscrupulous rogues and charlatans.

The society thrived at first with enthusiastic groups of members visiting:

hospitals, mental institutions, and schools in order to examine as many different types of hands as possible; they amassed a considerable collection of hand casts in plaster, and instituted a system of elementary examinations within the framework of the society.[4]

By 1892, membership figures justified the publication of a journal, *The Palmist's Review*, but by 1898 both journal and society had ceased to exist. There is little doubt that the practice of offering members services as hand readers at garden parties and fêtes, no matter how well-intentioned, went some way towards destroying the society's credibility.

The society's president, Katherine Ashton St Hill, and the treasurer, Ina Oxenford, went on to write several books on the subject of palmistry, among them one of the first claiming to deal specifically with medical palmistry for the benefit of the layman.

The mid-nineteenth to mid-twentieth centuries saw a veritable avalanche of works on all aspects of palmistry. More were published in this period than at any other time before or since. Some were original in concept, but most merely rehashed and regurgitated the outmoded and inadequate systems of yesteryear, albeit with a superficial, supposedly scientific veneer. Typical of this genre was Mrs Robinson's *The Graven Palm*, 'A Manual of the Science of Palmistry', published in 1911 and later reprinted. The book is little more than an advertisement for Mrs Robinson's talents as a professional palmist and is replete with fascinating anecdotes about her well-connected clients who were of 'all ranks and classes, from royalty downwards'.

Far worse was the 'unique work' written by the incredible Comte C. de Saint Germain, the self-styled 'President of the National School of Palmistry' and the 'American Chirological Society'. It is a book which cannot fail to mark the lowest ebb to which palmistry could fall – Saint Germain was a throwback to the palmistic equivalent of Neanderthal times. *The Practice of Palmistry for Professional Purposes* was first published in 1897 and has recently been reissued in its original form for the umpteenth time. According to the modest author, his aim was, purely and simply, to promote 'the Science of Palmistry' and 'guide the chiromants of either sex out of their discouraged meanderings to the blessed gate that opens into Daylight, Pure Air and – Truth.' Examples of his 'guidance' are reproduced in Figure 4. Heaven help those who *did* look to him as an authority especially if they were in need of a few positive words of encouragement. Saint Germain blatantly plagiarized the works of Katherine St Hill, Ina Oxenford and other members of the English Chirological Society, and actually launched his book under the supposed patronage of 'the great French chiromant' Desbarrolles who (by Saint Germain's own admission) was quite unable to have introduced the book, having died eleven years before!

At the same time, and also in America, William G. Benham had determined to approach the entire subject of palmistry as if no one had ever done so before. Ironically it was a meeting with a gipsy when Benham was a young man that sparked off the consuming passion to which he would devote his labours. In his own words, so as to:

prepare myself for a proper consideration of these matters, I studied medicine, so that I might be familiar with the entire anatomical construction of the body . . .[8]

He went on to study, by direct observation, the links between the hand and health (both mental and physical), character and self-determination. The essence of a lifetime's work was distilled into an instructional text which he titled *The Laws of Scientific Hand Reading*. No greater contrast to Saint Germain's manual for charlatans could be imagined.

Benham's efforts were based on his certainty that there was a scientific basis underlying the whole concept of hand analysis. He was one of the first to prophesy that some of palmistry's greatest and most important applications would be in the areas of vocational and marriage guidance.[6]

A prophecy which later research would amply fulfil.

It's difficult to know quite where in our catalogue to place the legendary 'Cheiro' (1866–1936), who also styled himself Count Louis Hamon. He was an Irishman with more than his fair share of the gift of the gab and his list of illustrious clients reads like a *Who's Who* of the day. His idealism and way with words is evident in his first book on

Figure 4   Examples of the Comte de Saint Germain's 'guidance'

If the star is faint and poorly formed —Ill health and trouble at the close of life.

Paralysis.—A star on Saturn. A star on the middle part of the Mount of the Moon; a very much rayed and crossed Mount of the Moon; and often a sloping Line of Head, while the Line of Heart starts from the Lines of Life and Head in fatal cases.

"The subject died at 36 from the consequences of sexual excesses."

A star almost in the middle of a double or triple Girdle of Venus—Terrible venereal disease, to be soon followed by death.

A star, with the line of fate entering deeply into the second finger—Danger of assassination. Should the hand be generally bad—Murderous tendency.

A circle—A favorable omen, specified

by other indications. (Very rare).

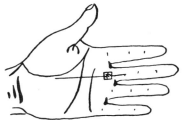

A square—Preservation from some great fatality read elsewhere in the hand.

A star within a square—Escape from assassination.

A square with red dots at the corners —Preservation of life in a fire.

palmistry, *The Language of the Hand*, which he wrote when he was only twenty-eight years of age. He was already renowned as a palmist and the first edition of five thousand copies sold in the space of four months. The titled and the wealthy flocked to his consulting rooms in London and New York on the strength of the accuracy of his predictions.

Sarah Bernhardt, Madame Melba, Ramon Novarro, Mark Twain, Swami Vivekananda, William Whiteley, Lord Russell of Killowen (then Lord Chief Justice of England), and an assortment of lords and ladies, politicians, military men, and even men of the cloth came to test out and to consult the oracle. Most of his clients professed themselves amazed by his accuracy and when it came to personal predictions, he seems to have been unequalled. How much of this was due to what he actually read from the hand, and how much to his phenomenal powers as a clairvoyant and seer is open to question. Cheiro was the Uri Geller of palmistry, full of charm and chat, but he bent rules instead of forks. There is no doubt that, even if he'd shown himself to be more scientifically minded, his extravagant persona and voracious ego would have made the 'Count' a controversial figure who did little to make palmistry respectable.

Dr N. Vaschide (1870–1907) worked hard during his short lifetime to gain scientific recognition for palmistry as an aid to psychological diagnosis. He became Assistant Director of the Laboratory of Pathological Psychology at the prestigious École des Hautes Études in Paris, and his book *Essai sur une Psychologie de la Main* was published in 1909, two years after his premature death at the age of thirty-seven. Vaschide is remembered chiefly for his theory concerning the *image motorique*. He believed that part of the brain is programmed, and the hand simultaneously imprinted with lines and marks, as a direct result of the innumerable movements we make – waking and sleeping, consciously and unconsciously. Vaschide, however, confined his theory to muscular sensibility, from which he distinguished sharply the hand's other sensory functions. Less than thirty years later, physiologists rejected his ideas on the grounds that,

discrimination between the different functions of the tactile sense is not possible. They are interdependent in function as well as in their cortical representation.[3]

Frederic Wood-Jones was Professor of Anatomy at the University of Manchester when he wrote *The Principles of Anatomy as seen in the Hand*. This classic work, published in 1919, is informative without being pedantic, and a joy to read for jargon is cut to the barest unavoidable minimum. In its field, admittedly specialist, it is unsurpassed to this day, and required reading for the serious student of the hand.

Wood-Jones was one of the first to suggest that there might be a specific relationship between individual parts of the hand, the rest of the body, and the cerebral cortex. His work on the hand led him to believe that:

> every area of the cortical region is connected with one or other of the five fingers. As the thumb seems to be related to the face, the fifth finger to the feet, we might expect that other sections of the body from head to toe would be correlated with the three other fingers.[3]

Medical doctors and physicians have of course used nonspecific signs in the hands and nails to back up diagnoses for centuries, and proponents of acupuncture, reflexology, and iridology expect to find correspondences between symptoms in one part of the body and another (see Figures 5, 6 and 7).

> Acupuncture, conservatively estimated to be more than 2,000 years old, is based on the concept that the human body has an internal set of channels – or meridians, as these are now called – with 365 points where the channels surface onto the skin. These meridians are places where control on yin and yang can best be exercised and effected . . .[9]

There is little doubt that Wood-Jones was influenced by the findings of his contemporary and compatriot, Sir Henry Head, the neurologist. The treatment zones discovered by Head still bear his name today, more than a hundred years on. They mark the birth in the West of therapeutic anaesthesia – a system corresponding remarkably closely with the tenets basic to acupuncture. The distribution of the meridians and the nervous system have a lot in common, researchers are discovering today.

Henri Mangin was a French chirologist who attempted, rather more successfully than most, to bridge the gap between palmistry and orthodox medicine. He studied the hand intensively for ten years, and collaborated with the medical profession in the production of articles and several books during the 1940s and 1950s. One of the most valuable as far as medical palmistry is concerned was *Valeur Clinique des Ongles*, which summarized his findings about the nails and their significance in diagnosis. There have been several editions, unfortunately for the non-linguist, all in French.

At about the same time, Dr Charlotte Wolff was taking the world of experimental psychology by storm. At pains to declare herself a scientist, and in no way influenced by the common or garden superstitions of mere palmistry, she readily admits that, historically speaking, 'occultism formed the basis of scientific discovery'. She was influenced by the earlier work of Carus and Vaschide and railed against the 'general indifference of physician's to the information which a patient's hand may furnish'.[3]

Dr Wolff worked in Paris, where she studied the hands of 'backward, nervous, and difficult children' and juvenile delinquents, and in London, where she researched normal subjects in an attempt to relate character and mentality with hand-markings. Previously, with the cooperation of the Royal Zoological Society, she had taken foot and hand prints of apes and monkeys with a view to placing the psychological study of man in its 'proper evolutionary perspective'. The results of this study were published in the form of two papers, in the *Proceedings of the Royal Zoological Society of London*, 1937 and 1938.

In her book *The Human Hand*, Dr Wolff gives a masterly exposition of her theory. Unfortunately, one has to suspect the potential objectivity of an author who fails to admit to a correlation with traditional palmistry where it exists, and whose quoted chirological associations are, at best, obscure. *All* palmists aren't 'gipsies, fortune-tellers and quacks' any more than *all* psychologists and doctors are inevitably scientists and automatically exempt from making mistakes, though according to Dr Wolff and her publisher, 'It is very doubtful if a palmist possessed of the qualifications of a scientist has yet existed.' There's nothing quite as unscientific as blind, blinkered prejudice but scientists as a body seem rather more prone to this failing than they ought to be. It's a pity, too, that Dr Wolff should risk her credibility to prove a point. She includes a print in her book which looks as if it owes rather more to artifice than nature. Drawing our attention to Plates 23 and 24, she says,

I conclude this book with this example because it affords such powerful evidence of a link between the crease-line system and the mind in general . . . The fact of a rare and striking change in one of the least mutable crease-lines is a positive indication not only of the diagnostic but of the prognostic value of hand-psychology.

I don't doubt that the *hand* had changed, but the print seems to have been crudely pencilled to emphasize the point.

Figure 5   A Chinese diagram illustrating some of the acupuncture meridians

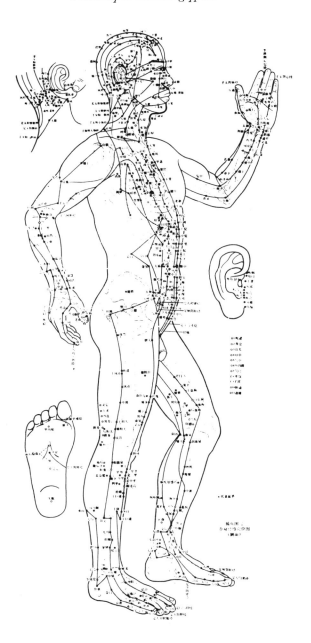

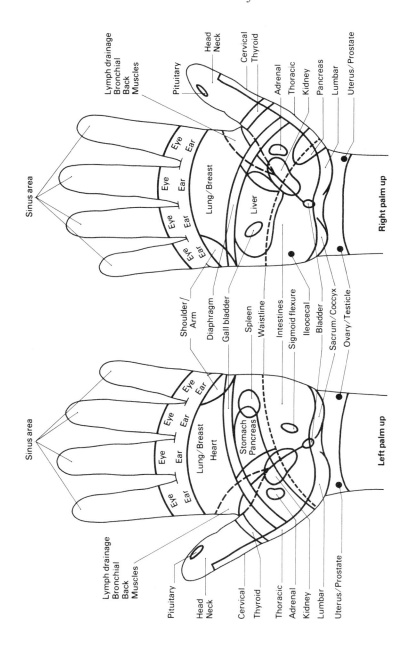

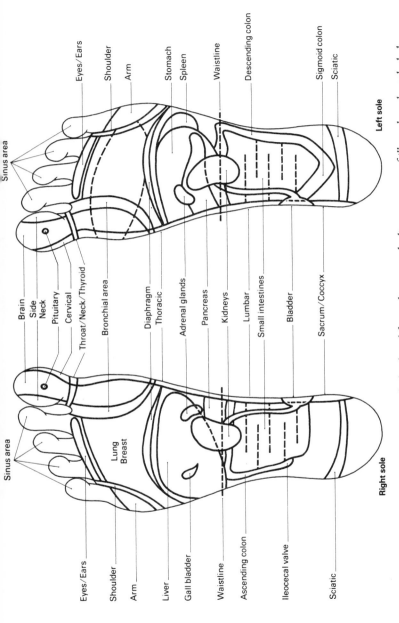

Figure 6   The reflexologist massages points on the hands and feet to diagnose and relieve symptoms of illness throughout the body

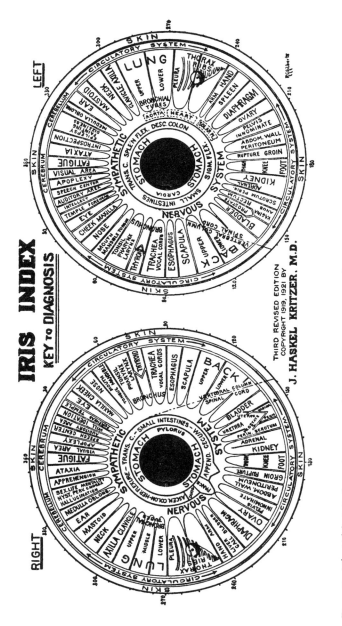

Figure 7   The iridologist's chart relating parts of the eye with parts of the body

Though she doesn't go out of her way to credit him, the work of Julius Spier seems also to have influenced Dr Wolff. Spier's lectures at Zurich University were sufficiently inspiring to impress C.G. Jung who wrote an introduction to *The Hands of Children*, the first of an intended trilogy summarizing Spier's work in the field of Psycho-Chirology. In Jung's view,

The findings and knowledge expounded in this book are of essential importance for psychologists, doctors, and educationalists. Spier's Chirology is a valuable contribution to character-research in its widest application.[10]

It was Spier's belief that a man's inheritance is shown very clearly in his hands, and that many neuroses could be avoided in later life by examining the hands of children early on. He was hopeful of teaching parents to allow their children to develop 'in accordance with their actual dispositions', rather than bringing them up 'according to the negative experiences of their own childhood', or trying to find 'the fulfilment of their own frustrated wishes in their child'.

Spier's greatest contribution to the science of palmistry was to suggest that inherited characteristics could be seen in the hands. It is a testimony to his faith and fervour that he made so many converts to psycho-chirology. The bulk of his research was done before the Second World War (he died before the war ended), and his book reflects the fact that, at that time, the scientific worker was still using traditional palmistic terminology. This alone would have antagonized many doctors and psychologists, causing the skeletal remains of the fortune-telling image to jingle-jangle in the closet again.

Spier's arrogance did little to endear him to his fellow chirologists, either. Quoting 'thirty years of practical experience' he blithely throws out a couple of hundred years' worth of observations as 'inaccurate and psychologically unfounded'. That other hand readers seem to have been correct according to their clients is dismissed as insubstantial evidence for the defence. All these readings would have been given to, Spier says,

persons who are only interested in static facts and events and, therefore, of a more or less undifferentiated intellectual and spiritual status and development.[10]

It's unfortunate but true that few researchers are genuinely unbiased, and statistics, as we're always being told, can easily be rigged to suit a particular bias. Human nature being what it is, when we're seeking to prove a point we have a blind spot. Our minds automatically blot out or play down the significance of data that might prejudice our theories – chirologists are not exempt from this failing, by any means!

Dr Hugo Debrunner, a Swiss, is another psychologist who saw the potential of hand analysis as a means of understanding his fellow man. In 1941, he carried out experimental tests with the cooperation of the Swiss army. These were designed to help assess the suitability of candidates for commission, or employment in intelligence units.

Candidates had to hold their hands level with their faces and were then photographed. Some held their palms forward and others seemed instinctively to hold their palms away from the camera. This more secretive group was considered by Debrunner to be better adapted towards security work. [11]

The results of these tests were compared with the results of others involving analysis of handwriting, 'doodles', dreams, and face and body structure. His work in the area of 'the psychology of gesture' has since been repeated and used as a model for more sophisticated studies.

Since 1950 he has extended his diagnostic researches on hand and foot structures on all ages right down to pre-natal development. In addition he examined members of various races and cultures and extended his studies to primates. The biological and anthropological researches incorporated also all the aspects of the papillary lines. [12]

Dr Debrunner's fine collection of hand- and foot-prints included more than 400 prints of apes but his published work, though extensive, is limited to papers and articles in the original German.

Noel Jaquin was not a medical man, but he was a natural psychologist with a deep and insatiable curiosity about human nature. He devoted his life to taking palmistry out of the realm of the occult and bringing it into the twentieth century as a science. It's difficult to judge the degree to which he was successful, but he gave those who took the trouble to listen to him much food for thought, and accurately foresaw the coming acceptance of palmistry as an aid to diagnosis:

The official recognition by medical men of the possibility of making any diagnosis from a mere examination of the hand may yet be many years ahead; but its recognition is inevitable because truth is always invincible. [13]

His dream was,

to see, one day, this study of the human hand ranking as a definite science, being used as an aid in the diagnosis of disease and to unravel the psychological tangles that so often bring disaster into human life. [2]

Jaquin as a young man fully intended to make a career for himself in medicine, taking his first steps in this direction very early on. He spent his pocket money on buying secondhand medical books and a microscope, and began to study diligently in his 'laboratory' at the top of the house, 'dissecting dead rats, breeding bacteria and doing all sorts of dangerous things – but all the time learning a great deal'. The Great War, as wars always do, put paid to his plans and economic necessity forced him to go into the family business instead. But not for long.

Palmistry had been a consuming hobby since, as a fourteen-year-old lad, he'd begun to study a book given him by an uncle. Gradually, it became more and more of an obsession, and Jaquin started a collection of prints of famous people of the day. Sir Arthur Keith, the anthropologist, obviously impressed by Jaquin's enthusiasm, provided an introduction to Sir James Galloway who gave him permission to examine the hands of patients at Charing Cross Hospital.

Years of study and cross-checking prints over an extended period of time proved to Jaquin that (a) the hand *did* change, and (b) that those changes were often, if not always, related to health and disease. He found that,

the hand did most definitely give indications of developing disease conditions and also showed inherited predispositions for disease when other, and more orthodox methods, were useless.[2]

In 1945, Jaquin was to found the Society for the Study of Physiological Patterns: a society which continues to flourish today. The Society's aims were, and are,

(a) To further the study of, and research into, the meaning and value of the Physiological Pattern as diagnostic evidence in psychological and pathological connections.
(b) To prove and stabilize the scientific importance of those studies.

It seems that Jaquin was unaware of the rather more orthodox research that was going on in America at the same time; research that was leading scientists in a similar direction.

A fellow and founder member of the SSPP, later elected President of the Society on Jaquin's death, was Beryl Hutchinson, MBE. Miss Hutchinson was cast in the same mould as her predecessor and her book, *Your Life in Your Hands*, reflects the energy and enthusiasm she was able to generate for her subject. The book summarizes current thinking on hand analysis up to 1967, includes chapters relating the hand to psychological and physical ill-health, and introduces her own well-researched findings on mineral imbalance as reflected in the human hand. Here, too, for the very first time outside a specialist text-book, we find a mention of dermatoglyphics.

Galton's pioneering work concerning the morphology, classification, inheritance and racial variation in fingerprints had stimulated the interest of anatomists, anthropologists, zoologists, geneticists, and criminal investigators the world over. In the United States of America, Harris Hawthorne Wilder (1864–1928) inaugurated,

a program of biological investigations with a study of comparative dermatoglyphics. His first paper on the subject was published in 1897, and in the following three decades he continued with studies devoted to morphology, the methodology of plantar and palmar dermatoglyphics, inheritance and racial differences.[5]

Wilder's wife, Inez Whipple Wilder, a former student of his, did much valuable work in her own right in the field, while important contributions to comparative dermatoglyphics were made by Schlaginhaufen and Kidd in the early 1900s. Kristin Bonnevie made a series of studies into the mechanisms of inheritance and embryological processes 'leading to the expression of particular configurations' in the twenties and thirties. Embryologists today still refer to her as an authority on the development of papillary ridge patterns. Heinrich Poll (1877–1939),

devised novel and revealing methods for the analysis of finger prints. He investigated racial differences, geographic variation within races, constitution and symmetry.[5]

The term dermatoglyphics, used to describe this 'new' science was coined in 1926 by Harold Cummins and Charles Midlo, of the Department of Microscopic Anatomy, Tulahe University. Their masterly exposition of the subject, *Fingerprints, Palms and Soles*, was first published in America in 1943. It is, justifiably, a classic work, essential to the library of anyone with a serious interest in the subject.

But why should our hands be the focus of so much interest? Why the hand, rather than any other organ in the human body? Before we can begin to appreciate any of the whys and wherefores of palmistry, medical palmistry, or dermatoglyphics perhaps we should try to clear from our minds any lingering prejudice based on the use of the hand as a vehicle for prediction. There must surely be more to it than that, or palmistry wouldn't have survived a year, let alone centuries of interest and persecution. The amazing possibility that our hands hold clues to our uniqueness – not just of character, personality and intellect, but also of our chemical and genetic make-up and health potential – shouldn't be arbitrarily dismissed. It must deserve our fullest attention, so let's go back to basics, and take a look at the hand in some detail: as a tool, as a marvellous feat of engineering, and as a part of the whole.

2

The Human Hand – Symbol of Man's Superiority

The hand adapts itself to the roughest work as well as to the most delicate. It has wielded with equal skill the flint knife of the primitive hunter, the blacksmith's hammer, the woodcutter's axe, the farmer's plough, the sword of the medieval knight, the controls of the modern aviator, the artist's brush, the journalist's pen, the threads of the silk-weaver. It is able to kill and to bless, to steal and to give, to throw grain on the surface of the fields and to throw grenades in the trenches.

Alexis Carrel, *Man the Unknown*[1]

Stop for a moment and consider your own hands. Can you envisage life without hands? How would you manage – would you even be able to cope at all? Whatever our position in society, be it manager, manual worker, housewife, clerk, or artist, we need hands! Because it's so obvious, the question seems slightly ridiculous, doesn't it? There are a myriad and one movements and manoeuvres – simple, complicated, and skilled – that we carry out daily. It's an ability that we take for granted, naturally enough, unless we or someone close to us is deprived of the facility. To think, as we say, is to act, and acting normally involves us in using our hands in some way. Even pondering a knotty problem may cause us to scratch our head, rub our brow, or wring our hands in desperation.

An abundance of commonly used expressions signifies our unconscious awareness of the important role our hands have to play. Let's look at a few. The word 'hand' can be used, for instance, to describe a style of writing, a worker normally hired for his manual abilities, a direction ('take the right-hand fork'), a share of the deck in a card game, or a unit of measurement based on an extremely generous hand's breadth of four inches or so. Figuratively speaking, we'll 'give someone a hand', or describe them as being 'hand-picked', 'handy', or 'handless' (meaning clumsy or awkward), and a person may be 'hand in glove' with a wrong-doer, or inadvertently 'show his hand', while a naughty child is often referred to as being a 'bit of a handful'.

The same child's parents may heave a sigh of relief when he is 'off their hands'. Especially if they've been living a 'hand-to-mouth' type of existence. There are second-hand, or hand-me-down goods, and we might win a contest 'hands-down', keep something 'in hand' for later, or work 'hand-in-hand' with someone. And we all know people who are high, even heavy-handed, or always trying to get the 'upper hand'. Who'll never be found going 'cap in hand' to anyone, though they might well 'wash their hands' of responsibility if things happened to go wrong.

Unless we injure or lose the use of our hands it's easy enough to take them for granted. Yet we'll marvel at the skill of a computer-controlled robot arm with its relatively clumsy fingering movements, the dexterity of a monkey swinging through the forest or peeling an orange or banana at the zoo, or the adroitness of a squirrel, rat, or hamster as it daintily nibbles a nut or other rodent delicacy. The instinctive dexterity of such animals, however, fades into insignificance beside that of the human hand when it is directed by the highest human intelligence.

The hand has been described as 'a visible part of the brain' and it may surprise you to learn that this is no poetic flight of fancy, for:

the whole of the central nervous system is merely an inturned portion of the general surface of the embryonic body. . . Now this is a very curious thing, that our brains and the whole of our nervous systems should be developed from that embryonic layer which, when remaining in its original site, simply gives rise to our skin. [We can therefore . . .] regard the central nervous system as no more than a buried portion of skin, or, alternatively, we may look upon the skin as an exposed portion of the central nervous system.[14]

The most elementary of all sense organs, in man or beast, is the skin. In evolved man, sensitivity is localized and considerably heightened in the facial area (particularly round the mouth), the palms of the hands, and, to a lesser degree, on the soles of the feet.

Because the hands *are* so closely linked with the brain, trying to imagine life without them is virtually impossible: almost as impossible as imagining life without breathing! More often than not, the thinking and the doing are simultaneous, part of a smoothly integrated and indivisible process. Eating, drinking, sitting down, getting up, all involve a series of coordinated movements: movements that would have us tied in knots if we had to consciously plan which muscles to use, and in which order!

Anyone who has tried to learn golf or to hold reins will know how stupid muscles make themselves when under direct instruction from the conscious Will. They will also know the relief when, having finally shown them what we want we can just say to the ball, not to our body – 'proceed to yonder flag.'[15]

Although the process is barely understood, thoughts are known to trigger chemical or electrical responses in the body:

according to these impulses the molecules start to rearrange themselves. [. . . In this way] one can see how thought can influence the human field and the actual growth of the body. . . . Thus the character of man, his mental habits, should be definitely reflected in the body, in his way of moving, in his eyes, on his face, hands and so on.[16]

Clinical ecologists have proved mental and behavioural reactions of allergic origin to be extremely common. Any chemical, however ingested, may trigger an adverse reaction in susceptible persons – often on or through the central nervous system. Such reactions are invariably signposted in the hands, as we shall see later, whether in the form of breakdown of the skin ridge patterns, pathological changes in the lines, or trembling, lack of coordination, and paralysis.

   Losing the use of our hands (or indeed that of any other sense) drastically reduces our ability to function successfully as an independent unit in society, and it's a loss that would be none the less devastating for a Beethoven, a bus-driver, a bull-fighter, a ballet dancer, or a burglar. Of all the senses, the sense of touch is the most adaptable. The hands can become the eyes of the blind, and the mouth and ears of the deaf and dumb with comparative facility. Despite her handicaps, Helen Keller became social worker, author, and inspiration to millions.

The hand has advantages over the eye because it can observe the environment by means of touch, and having observed it, it can immediately proceed to do something about it. The hand has other great advantages over the eye. It can see round corners and it can see in the dark.[17]

Long before a child has learned to speak, he is able to communicate nonverbally by gesticulating and pointing. Usually, by the age of eighteen months or so, he has the language of gesture down to a fine art, and a few simple words besides. Even when he has learned to talk, gesture will continue to play its part in his vocabulary to a greater or lesser degree, depending on the particular mores of the race and culture into which he has been born. But it isn't only the Latins who are gifted with the ability to express their moods with their hands. We all do it. As often as not without realizing we've given anything away.

Watch a child as he's learning to read, laboriously following the printed word with an anxious finger. Writing, of course, involves the hand in more complicated manoeuvres, but, like riding a bicycle, it's an art that, once learned, is never forgotten (though in some illnesses it may become difficult, or impossible). The formula for action has been indelibly impressed on the brain, like instructions on a printed circuit.

Over an evolutionary period of many thousands of years the sensory fibres of the palm and fingers, used incessantly to amplify the mental images furnished by the eyes, have become intricately elaborated, and . . . it is no exaggeration to say that a considerable part of man's knowledge of the exterior world has been acquired through them.[3]

In a blind person – especially if that person was born blind – the hands can actually take over the function of the eyes, as we've already noted. To the newly blind, it soon becomes second nature to use the hands to effect a measure of control over an environment that has suddenly become alien and potentially dangerous. Sensitivity may be heightened to an incredible degree, leading to the development of seemingly bizarre abilities. Well-documented cases record sightless individuals correctly identifying, and differentiating between, a variety of colours with their hands alone. This has led to experiments being carried out under strict laboratory conditions in an attempt to discover whether this facility is latent in us all, or just a minority.

It's this same sense of touch that enables us as very young children to become aware of the three-dimensional nature of our surroundings. The word 'tangible' itself, meaning solid, or substantial, has its roots in the Latin, *tangere*, to touch. The Montessori educational system uses this growing awareness to ground three- and four-year-olds in the three 'Rs' by giving them colourful solid blocks, letters and figures to work with. As we become older, we refine this ability to assess objects until judging distance, depth, stability, cold and heat becomes a matter of reflex. One's survival might depend on having such information, literally, at one's fingertips.

The sign language that enables the deaf and dumb to converse in such a fluent and lively manner turns the hands into ballet dancers. Their miming allows the hands to replace both the ear and the voice – just as in tracing out and interpreting Braille dots they can pinch hit for the eye. Without personal experience of sensory deprivation it's impossible to appreciate the trauma that follows – or what it means to become part of the world again after even a short period of being cut off. It's a shadowy insubstantial place without the sense of touch, for the third dimension only becomes real for us as a direct result of tactual exploration, and through the vivid mental images that take shape as we reach out to feel, taste, smell, see, hear and embrace it.

Aeons of evolutionary progress have seen the human hand develop as

Figure 8 Relative motor and sensory representation in the human cortex

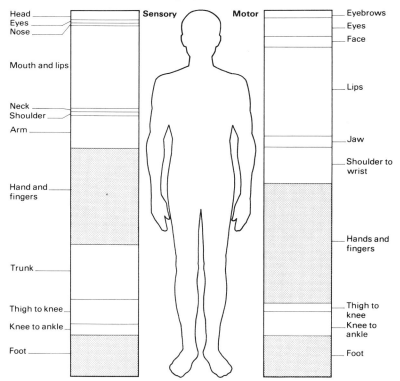

one of the most important sensory organs in the body, and this is reflected in the large area allotted to it in the cerebral cortex. Relatively speaking, the hands grab what at first sight appears to be a disproportionate share of cortical representation (see Figure 8).

A low mammal first gains its impressions of the world by its sense of smell; it tests the world with its nose. Not only is the olfactory sense a guiding one . . . but the tactile sensations of the snout region, of the lips and tongue, are soon added as sources of information wherewith to learn of novel objects. The snout region therefore gains cortical representation as a feeling and moving part of the body.

And,

The primitive arboreal animal learns of the world and tests novel objects with its eyes and its hands. A large visual area in the cortex and a large area for the awareness and the movements of the hands are therefore typical of such an animal. It is notable that in the human brain the large hand area is situated immediately adjacent to the older area in which sensations and movements of the face are represented.[14]

Vast numbers of nerve fibres interpenetrate the human organism, linking every last outpost of their dominion with the control centres in the brain. From the very first moment of consciousness to the very last a perpetual stream of data floods these centres where it's decoded, analysed and immediately acted upon. The nerve endings are concentrated in high-risk areas such as hand, foot and mouth – those organs that keep us 'in touch' with the world.

The cerebral parts of the hand, the tongue and the larynx extend over a large area of the brain surface. At the same time that the nervous centres control writing, speaking and the grasping and handling of objects, they are, in return, stimulated by these acts. Simultaneously, they are determining and determined.[1]

Man's rate of advance along the evolutionary spiral runs parallel to the degree to which he has developed a consciousness of his individuality: a sense of his separate identity. He no longer has to run with the common herd, and in order to survive has had to develop a different sort of awareness about his environment. This consciousness and the growth of his independence is reflected, as far as the human hand is concerned, in the development of his thumb.

    In evolving Man, this has meant an increasing ability in the thumb to oppose the other digits, together with a tendency to greater length. It's an ability that was limited in his forebears, and which remains undeveloped, or underdeveloped in the primates. Compare the human and chimpanzee hands in Figures 9 and 10.

The primates (with very few exceptions) show some degree of functional independence of the thumb, although the extent and precision of its movements differs considerably between the members of the Order. One can see a steady advance in the functional complexity of living primates from the lower primates (lemurs and lorises) to the higher primates (monkeys and apes) and finally to man. Monkeys are more adept than lemurs, apes are more adept than most of the monkeys, and man is more proficient still.[17]

The greater this opposition between thumb and fingers, the more potentially dextrous the individual, with the degree of opposability being entirely dependant on the relative length of thumb to fingers. In man there is a broader area of intimate contact possible between the tips of the fingers and the tip of the opposing thumbs (Figure 11) than there is in any of the primates.

Figure 9   A human hand (left) and a chimpanzee's

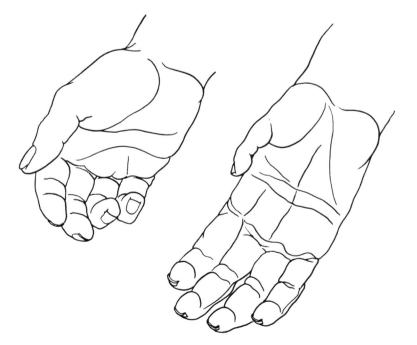

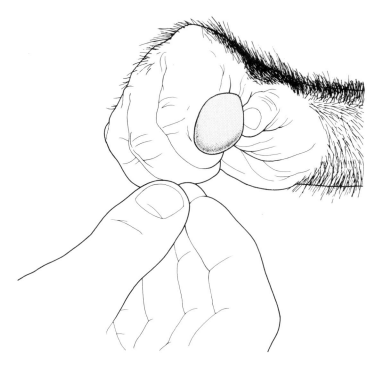

Figure 10 *Different degrees of opposition. The drawing shows opposition at work*
Figure 11 *Opposition at play*

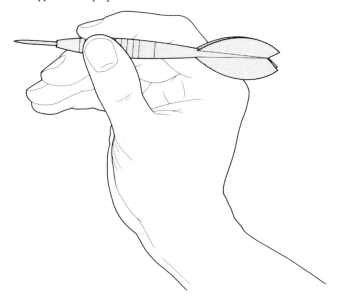

It is this opposability, and the finely textured nature of the skin covering fingers and palms taken together which give man his superiority over the animal kingdom. The thumb's flexibility, added to the special qualities of the papillary ridges, initially gave him the ability to grip, use, and later to design tools. The power to reason and to plan ahead gradually developed from this growing ability.

The thumb, more than anything else in the hand, has come to symbolize man's mastery over matter. Indeed,

Had it not been for the unique manner of the thumb's development in man, humanity as we know it would not have evolved, and that colossal jump from holding and throwing stones to manufacturing interstellar spacecraft could never have been made.[6]

Without a thumb at all, the hand is,

at worst, nothing but an animated fish slice, and at best a pair of forceps whose points don't meet properly. Without the thumb, the hand is put back sixty million years in evolutionary terms to a stage when the thumb had no independent movement and was just another digit.[17]

Man's superior intellect and the size of his brain – proportionately larger in terms of body size and weight than that of either the primates or his own antecedents – are both considered to be directly related to his developing hand-skills, though the crucial step between taking a naturally occurring object and putting it to use as a sort of makeshift tool as many animals are known to do, and setting out to modify or actually produce an artefact for a specific purpose didn't happen overnight. There was no inspired Neanderthal genius to shout a joyful 'Eureka!' to his fellows when he invented the wheel, for the capacity to envisage its versatility and potential would have been entirely lacking.

Many millions of years of evolution were to pass before primitive man made that vital breakthrough from being a tool-user to a tool-maker. Vital for the development of modern man, that is, for it was a process that taught him how to plan ahead. Human bones and simple tools dating from at least 1.75 million years ago were found at Olduvai Gorge in Tanzania in 1960 by Louis and Mary Leakey. This is the earliest recorded specimen of *Homo habilis*, or 'handyman'. It's as well to recall though that there would have been a considerable period of overlap during which handyman's ancestors concentrated solely on modifications of impromptu tools – simple improvements – before they were able to actually design tools for specific tasks.

Tool-making skill . . . depends on the proportions of the hand as well as the size and complexity of the cerebral cortex . . . [An] increase in brain size . . . is more likely to have followed than preceded tool-making, so that a positive feed-back became established. A breakthrough in tool-making is followed by an increase in the size and complexity of the cerebral hemispheres which is in turn followed by further advances in tool-making.[17]

The inexorable pressure exerted on the early tool-makers by the interminable process of natural selection pushed those with well-developed hand-skills to the evolutionary forefront, while the laggards fell further and further behind or became extinct. The special characteristics of the human cortex encourage the belief that the capacity for speech developed *after* and not before hand-skills, and that this in its turn:

led to the development of increasingly complex thinking and reasoning, and ultimately to man's using his brain in the way we all do today.[18]

Without doubt, the hand is a remarkable instrument. Yet its full potential – like that of the human intellect – has still to be revealed: as marvellous an instrument as the hand is, that potential cannot exceed the capacity of its master – the brain. Though the hands of two men may be almost identical as regards size, shape and dimension, if one is a normal, healthy individual and the other suffering chromosomal abnormalities, or his nervous system for some reason isn't functioning as it should, the hands of the two men will hold definite clues to their condition.

   The hands of a brain-damaged child, one affected by Down's syndrome, or an individual temporarily incapacitated by mental illness, depression, or alcoholism, will invariably betray the state of their owner's mind. This may show up in the lines and skin ridges, the way the hands are habitually held, or both – a dull mind will always reveal itself in limp, lifeless gestures, while a lively hand always betokens a lively mind:

The basis for skill doesn't lie in the hand. There are rogue cars that have to have engines replaced within the first few weeks of ownership, but there are no rogue hands. The skill of the hand lies in the brain and it is here that dexterity and adroitness (and clumsiness) originate. The hand is a mirror of the brain, therefore there can be no such combination as dextrous hands and clumsy brains.[17]

The human hand is as versatile as the mind controlling it. It can be the primary vehicle for the expression of mood and feeling, and used to slap or caress, to comfort or punish. And it can become an instrument of healing – watch a mother with a sick child, or a sympathetic nurse with a sick patient. Think of the delicate movements of a neuro-surgeon or a watchmaker, observe a woodman with his axe, a potter at the wheel, an artist at his easel. Pick up a pin, thread a needle, test your ability to differentiate between a number of different textures and temperatures – and marvel at the strength and versatility built into every pair of hands.

Our hands are symbolic of the superiority of man as a species, and they give the measure of our personal idiosyncrasies to anyone who is willing to learn to interpret the hieroglyphics that are written there. As we know, no two hands – even in the same individual – are ever exactly the same, and, if the medical research worker and the hand analyst are correct, our hands hold a treasury of hidden clues to our inheritance – our talents and our failings, our weaknesses and strengths, and our physical and mental constitution, now and in the years to come. It is because each of us react, in any given situation, in a slightly different way from our neighbour, and because our hands seem to play a vital role in the expression of our individuality, that attention – both scientific and esoteric – has focused on them down the centuries.

Let's take the next step in our investigation into this intriguing subject and look at the hand from an anatomical point of view. Perhaps an objective and dispassionate examination of its basic structure and its relationship with the human organism as a whole will give some perspective to the inquiry, and help us to understand how it might indeed be possible for the human hand to reflect character and potential, at the same time allowing the dermatoglyphic expert to diagnose and predict disorders, diseases and deficiencies.

3

The Structure of the Hand

The hand is a masterpiece. Simultaneously, it feels and it acts. It
acts as if endowed with sight. Owing to the unique properties of
its skin, its tactile nerves, its muscles, and its bones, the hand is
capable of manufacturing arms and tools. We would never have
acquired our mastery over matter without the aid of our fingers,
those five small levers, each composed of three articulated segments, which are mounted upon the metacarpus and the bones of
the wrist.

Alexis Carrel, *Man the Unknown*[1]

In purely mechanical terms the hand is a marvel of engineering. It's a
complex jigsaw of bone connected, sheathed and protected by muscle
and ligament, gristle and fascia, the whole enclosed within a supremely
sensitive, impermeable cover which is itself made up of three layers. Each
and every component in the body is an integral part of the whole – a fact
so obvious you may wonder at its being restated. It's a fact, though,
that's frequently ignored. Like the five blind men absorbed in their
examination of the elephant, each scientific discipline is convinced that
it, and it alone, is on the track of what really makes us tick. One blind
man is intent on the little curly tail, another the trunk, while the rest
limit themselves to ear, flank, and foot respectively. Each can insist that
the bit *he*'s looking at *is* the elephant. Or they can pool their information
in order to get a realistic idea of the animal's appearance. Man, however,
seems to be the sum of his parts and more . . .

all these sciences arrive at a different conception of their common object. They
abstract only from man what is attainable by their special methods. And those
abstractions, after they have been added together are still less rich than the con-
crete fact. They leave behind them a residue too important to be neglected.
Anatomy, chemistry, physiology, psychology, pedagogy, history, sociology,
political economy do not exhaust their subject.[1]

In examining the structure of the hand we should bear in mind the fact that no member, organ, or individual cell functions independently, but is designed to serve the whole and be served by it. Sickness and disease aren't limited to the part or organ that appears to be affected, but the intricate workings of flesh and blood, mind and spirit, body and soul are only just beginning to be understood. The natural inclination of a human organism, under all but the most unfavourable circumstances, is to strive – often against tremendous odds – for health. This is true whether or not we are able to comprehend the mechanisms involved.

Abstractions, the 'matter of scientific reasoning' can never hope to encompass the ultimate nature of things. We tend to look at science and scientists as the uninitiated used, in days gone by, to revere the High Priest, yet science is no more nor less than a systematic search for tangible proof of theories and basic principles. It has always tended to exclude from serious consideration such traditional 'tomfooleries' as palmistry, astrology and the like, though there's little doubt that there *are* laws governing such phenomena as clairvoyance, telepathy, psychometry, psycho-kinesis and other so-called extrasensory perceptions. Blind prejudice, however, often masquerades as pure science, and scientists with the courage and confidence to maintain open minds are few and far between. Unfortunately, it's also true that most palmists know very little about the anatomy and physiology of the hand.

With rare exceptions the adult human skeleton consists of 206 bones, 54 of these in the hands, slightly over 25 per cent of the total, (Figure 13). There are 14 finger bones (phalanges) in each hand, 5 palm bones (metacarpals), and 8 wrist bones (carpals). The same phalangeal formula is common to all mammals with the thumb having two visible joints and the remaining digits three joints.

Normally, the bones in the human frame are fully developed by the time the individual is twenty-five years old. All bone starts out as gristle (or cartilage) in the foetus which has, of necessity, to remain flexible. In the mature man and woman cartilage remains in only a few areas such as the ears, nose and throat, and the moving surfaces of some joints. In the adult, mobility and flexibility of hands and feet are achieved by means of synovial joints, muscles and ligaments.

The synovial sac or bursa is filled with a clear fluid, a buffering agent which allows the joints to move freely and without friction. For added protection and ease of movement there's a thin layer of articular cartilage, strong and elastic, covering the bone-ends. Tennis elbow and

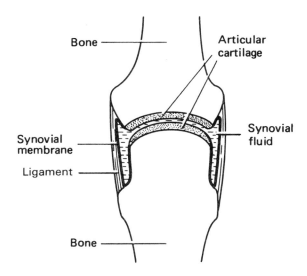

Figure 12   A typical synovial joint

housemaid's knee are the painful result of damage to the synovial joints in two areas which are particularly vulnerable. The synovial is the most common joint in the body, with four modifications represented in the hand. These are the hinge-joint, the saddle-joint, the bi-axial joint, and the plane-joint. Each modification, as its name suggests, represents a slightly different range of movement enabling the fingers to be curled into the palm, or straightened, flexed from side to side, and rotated slightly (see Figure 12).

Without some element of control, this movement would be at best extremely clumsy. Mobility is dependent on the quality of muscles and ligaments, and of course the nervous system controlling them. In certain illnesses, where these functions are impaired, the limbs can no longer respond to signals from the brain and instead flail uncontrollably, or fail to move at all.

Muscle coordination is dependent on the inter-action of many organs. Skeletal, that is to say voluntary, muscles:

receive their orders from the central nervous system, and their energy from the heart, the lungs, the endocrine glands, and the blood. To carry out the directions of the brain they demand the help of the whole body.[1]

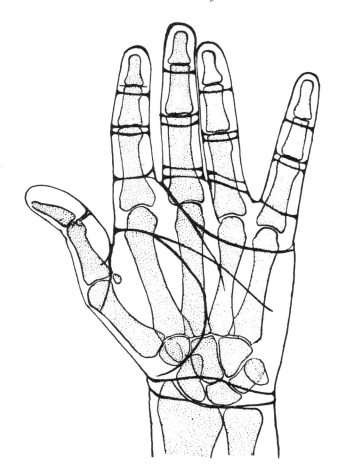

Figure 13   Lines of the palm, shown in relation to the bony structure of the hand

The musculature of hands and feet is necessarily more compact than else-where in the body. The controlling mechanisms are condensed into a smaller space, yet must remain flexible and dextrous at all times. The muscle structure at front and back of the hand is shown in Figures 14, 15 and 16.

The muscles on the palm side of the hand are mostly concerned with gripping and grasping. They are therefore known as flexors. Those on the dorsal side of the hand enable us to open our fists, straighten our fingers, stretch them, and are known as extensors. The bulky pads under the thumbs and little fingers – thenar and hypothenar eminences respectively – are made up of muscle and fatty fibrous tissue which helps protect the delicate underlying structure from injury.

There is tremendous variation in the depth and consistency of these pads from person to person. It is of course on such individual variations. that the palmist bases his analyses. Professor John Napier describes the

Figure 14   The palm of the hand, showing interosseous musculature

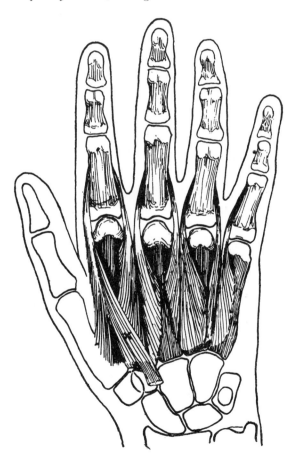

physical examination undergone by German concentration camp survivors in 1945:

most of them had used up all their available stored fat, even from the walls of the heart. Yet in spite of the fact that the prisoners were little more than walking skeletons, their heel pads were intact, rounded and as fatty as ever . . .[17]

Figure 15   Palmar view of a dissection of the hand

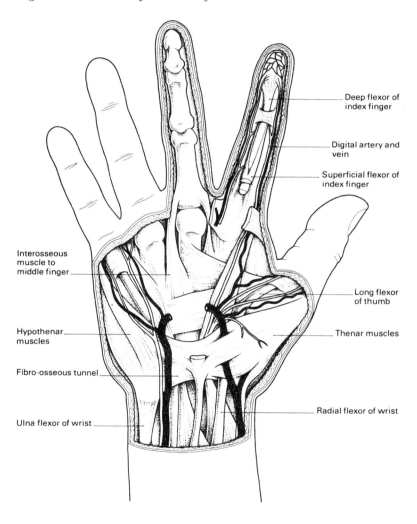

Deep flexor of index finger

Digital artery and vein

Superficial flexor of index finger

Interosseous muscle to middle finger

Long flexor of thumb

Hypothenar muscles

Thenar muscles

Fibro-osseous tunnel

Radial flexor of wrist

Ulna flexor of wrist

The Professor was obviously unaware that palmistic tradition associates well-developed mounts in this area with a creative, positive-thinking nature and a strong and durable constitution. The firm springy mount,

shows a corresponding resilience of character and suggests hidden reserves of energy. This type of mount goes with a forceful and dynamic personality . . .[6]

Figure 16   Dorsal view

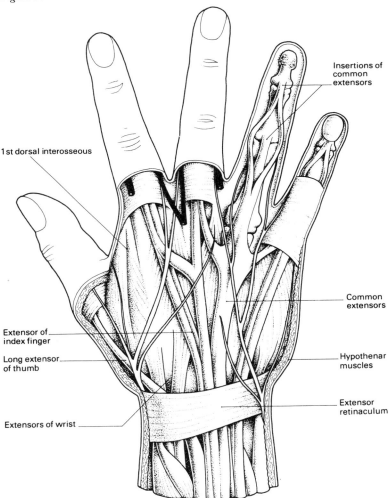

Insertions of common extensors

1st dorsal interosseous

Common extensors

Extensor of index finger

Long extensor of thumb

Hypothenar muscles

Extensor retinaculum

Extensors of wrist

Just the sort of person, in fact, you'd expect to be a survivor!

Apart from the flexors, both superficial and deep, and the extensors, there are other, shorter muscles in the hand known as the *interosseus* (Figure 15) and the *lumbrical*. These are muscles which control the base phalanges of the fingers, and are well provided with specialized nerve-endings giving a positional sense unequalled elsewhere in the body.

Dr Charlotte Wolff, the psychologist with a particular interest in hands, found that,

Figure 17   Deep and superficial palmar arches

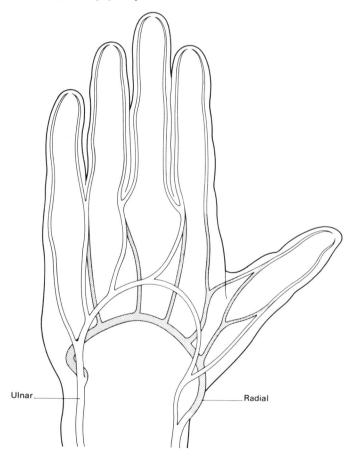

Ulnar_____   _____ Radial

Generally speaking, forward movements (initiated primarily by the flexors) correspond to positive impulses and are connected with a feeling of ease and self-extension, while movements of withdrawal (initiated by the extensors) go with inhibition and retirement.[3]

These findings have since been confirmed and amplified by many similar studies of 'body-language'.

The blood supply to the hand is elaborate and enters at two points. There is the Ulnar artery (see Figure 17) which branches upwards,

Figure 18   Typical veinous arrangement on the back of the hand

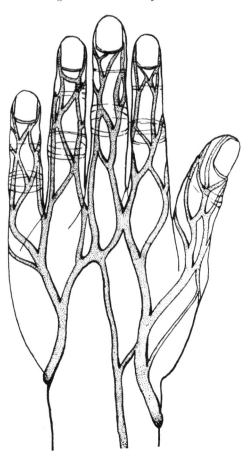

separating on the way into digital arteries. These, in turn, fan out to form the fine network of blood vessels, veins and capillaries that irrigates and feeds the fingers so efficiently. The point at the wrist where we traditionally check our pulse marks the entrance into the hand of the Radial artery. The Ulnar artery enters from the opposite side of the wrist, and the two interlace, forming the deep and superficial palmar arches.

There are characteristic individual variations between one hand and another, and anatomists and chirologists alike are in agreement that,

Although venous channels preserve a definite degree of physiological or functional uniformity in their main distribution, the anatomical disposition of their actual branches is subject to a very wide degree of variation.[14]

One of the first signs of anaemia, whatever the basic cause, is blueness of the fingertips, showing that the blood isn't being properly oxygenated. Another symptom may be brittle fingernails, accompanied by longitudinal ridging. A return to health will be signalled by a rosy glow in both the cheeks and fingertips.

The lymphatic system serving the hands is equally complex, as Figure 19 shows. It will be noted that the lymphatic vessels are concentrated at precisely those points at the back of the hand that are likely to be most vulnerable to injury, namely the knuckles and finger tips. For some reason, the lymphatic channels serving the back of the thumb and the index finger, and the space between, bypass the lymph nodes in the arm, carrying on till they reach those above the collarbone. Because of this, there is a superstitious belief that wounds affecting the radial side of the hand don't heal as quickly as those on the ulnar side. This may or may not be so, but certainly the lymphocytes rushing to an emergency on the thumb side of the hand have further to travel than those summoned to the other side.

The bones and muscles, veins and arteries are enveloped and interpenetrated by layers of flexible, fibrous connective tissue, known as fascia (see Figures 20 and 21). There are two different types. The deep fascia supports and holds the constituent parts of the hand in place, gently but firmly – rather like an elastic stocking as worn for varicose conditions. This deep fascia is also vitally necessary to prevent the blood collecting and stagnating in susceptible areas:

The muscles are the great reservoirs of blood when the limbs are passive, and, therefore, around all the distensible muscles a firm sleeve of fascia is placed to resist the passive gravitation of fluids. Deep fascial investments of the limbs are present largely to resist passive fluid pressure.[14]

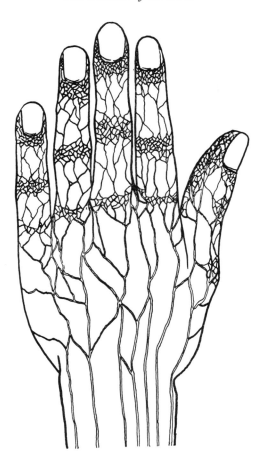

Figure 19   Lymphatic system shown on the back of the hand

The finger tips, the point where fingers join the palm, and the junction of palm and wrist are particularly well-endowed with superficial fascia, the second type. This is the fatty layer of subcutaneous tissue which insulates the entire body in varying degrees of thickness, preventing heat loss, and protecting delicate underlying structures and organs. The superficial fascia is interpenetrated by a vast network of capillary blood vessels and nerves on their way to and from the skin, carrying nourishment and discharging wastes, and transmitting and receiving information about the external environment beyond the epidermal barrier.

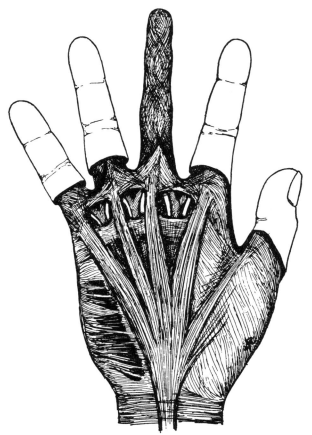

Figure 20   Palmar fascias

Every hand is different and individual variations in thickness or firm-
ness of the palm and its separate mounts, or pads, depend on the density
of the fascia, deep and superficial.

Immediately above this layer of connective tissue is the dermis, the soft
inner area where cells are constantly growing and multiplying. They
work their way up to the surface to replace the innumerable superficial
cells which are lost in the daily sloughing-off process. Blood vessels and
nerves continue their journey, accompanied now by sweat glands, hair
follicles, and sebaceous glands on the back of the hand, and sweat glands

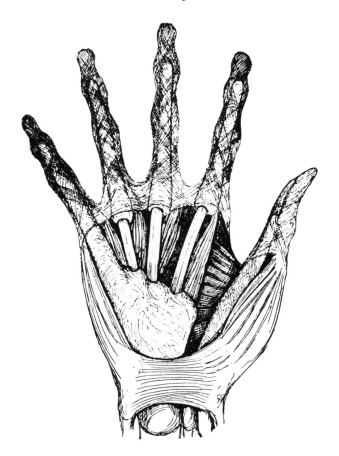

Figure 21   Palmar bursa and flexor tendon sheaths

and specialized nerve endings on the palm side of the hand. These sensory receptors are remarkable in that their structure varies depending on their specific function (see Figure 22). The simplest nerve endings are responsible for detecting pain and measuring heat or cold. Others, more complex, are able to register and differentiate between touch and pressure, the light play of a breeze on the skin, and the relative position of the hand and fingers. The hand and foot between them account for well over a third of the body's total sensory input, with only the lips and parts of the face being more sensitive (see Figure 8).

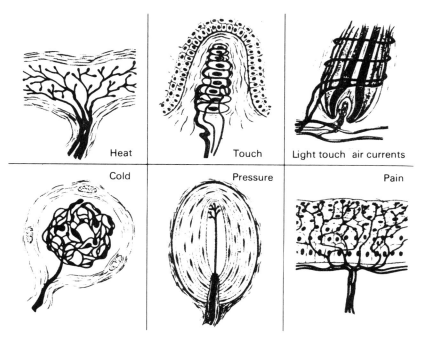

Figure 22　Diagrams to show the different structures of sensory receptors

Finger and toe nails enhance this sensitivity, besides shielding the delicate finger tips from injury. Press the top of a table lightly but firmly with the tip of the thumb or index finger, then compare the sensation when a similar degree of pressure is applied to the base of the thumb or another part of the palmar surface. It is this acute sensitivity that enables a blind person to learn Braille. The Braille alphabet represents each letter by a different arrangement of one to six slightly raised dots. Once learned, it's a simple matter for the blind person to run his fingers quickly over the printed page which he can often read as fast as most people with normal sight.

Each of our finger tips is made up of an incredibly complex arrangement of capillaries, veins, arteries, glands and nerve fibres, which branch vigorously upwards for all the world like a little tree (see Figure 23). The finger nail is yet another miracle of design (see Figure 24). Not only does it protect the finger tip and enhance overall sensitivity, it provides a convenient 'built-in tool-kit of cutters and pliers, scrapers and screw-

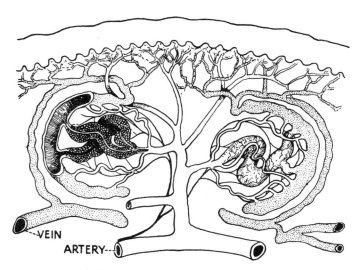

Figure 23   Part of the blood supply to the pad and tip of the finger

drivers'![17]. A colony of specialized cells is responsible for renewing this horny sheath, and takes an average of six months to do it. The thumb nail normally has a quicker growth rate and according to Wood-Jones the nails on the right hand in a right-handed individual tend to grow more quickly than those on the left. Abnormalities of the nails have provided doctors with clues to specific ailments since the days of Hippocrates, and will be discussed in more detail in later pages.

Figure 24   The structure of the finger nail

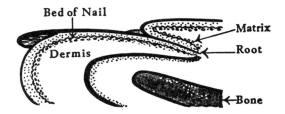

Up to this point in our discussion both the scientists – physiologists, anatomists, biologists and their ilk – and the informed palm reader with a scientific bent will be in total agreement regarding the development and mechanical functioning of the hand. Departures from this norm, though, are inevitably the province of the specialist. Cases involving missing or extra digits, phalanges, or toes, congenital fusing of bones, webbing of fingers and/or toes, and other, more severe, skeletal malformations are rare (see Figure 25), and it's extremely unlikely that they'd come to the notice of the average palmist. They are, however, far less unusual than they used to be.

Specific and identifiable chromosomal abnormalities are suspected in such cases, which may be triggered iatrogenically (as with the drug, thalidomide), or otherwise. Often, the causes of genetic damage in the embryo remain obscure, but it seems that a major role for dermatoglyphicists in the future will be in the area of genetic counselling, helping to identify chromosomal aberrations in the would-be parents and advising on the possibility of bearing a healthy or malformed baby. It is already being used in West Germany for this purpose.

It's when we start to look more deeply into the palmar markings – the lines and skin-ridge patterns – that controversy begins to rage and battle lines to be drawn. Scientists and chirologists hold widely differing views on the purpose and meaning of these mysterious patterns, and the flexure or 'crease' lines of the anatomist become 'Head', 'Heart', 'Life', and 'Fate' lines to the traditional palmist. All sciences have a vocabulary of their own, and dermatoglyphics is certainly no exception! But there is a danger here, the very real danger that specialization and the jargon that goes with it will isolate and sterilize ideas and concepts that belong to the human race as a whole. Intelligent general discussion will always provide a kinder climate, and fertile ground in which such ideas can happily bear fruit.

Dermatoglyphics, with its three-hundred-year history, is an example of what can happen. It is truly the hidden science, and particularly deserving of the attention of a wider audience for,

Each of us carries a number of harmful genes and may develop a genetic disorder or transmit one to our children. Every disease is either caused or influenced by genetic mechanisms. Common examples include heart disease, high blood pressure, cancer, diabetes, and allergies.[19]

Though we don't yet know exactly *what* is inherited – an actual physical defect, a pattern of reacting, a disposition – we do know that many

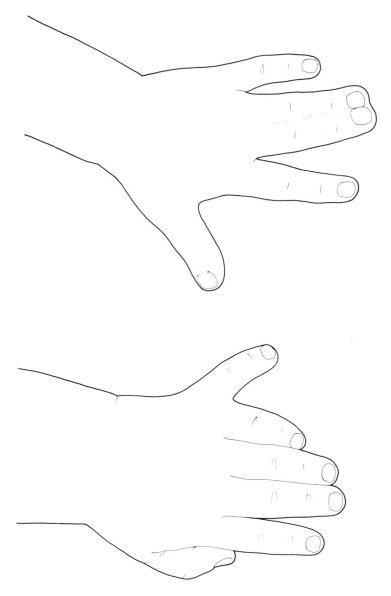

Figure 25

genetically induced disorders can be identified from the fingerprint and palmar markings on the patient's hands. The implications of this are staggering if not downright revolutionary. Dermatoglyphics could be the most unlikely, and inexpensive, weapon in the fight against disease yet discovered. To the trained expert, the skin-ridge patterns may eventually provide a blueprint of all our weak spots with the obvious advantage that preventive measures could then be introduced in time to halt or reverse the trend, or even to forestall it completely.

Why the human hand should be so informative is still a mystery but research into the lines and ridge patterns continues, worldwide, with Britain, West Germany and America leading the way.

4

The Lines and their Development

The concept of an average, the equation to a curve, the description of a froth or cellular tissue, all come within the scope of mathematics for no other reason than that they are summations of more elementary principles or phenomena. Growth and Form are throughout of this composite nature; therefore the laws of mathematics are bound to underlie them, and her methods to be peculiarly fitted to interpret them.

For one reason or another there are very many organic forms which we cannot describe, still less define, in mathematical terms . . . But we may already use mathematical language to describe, even to define in general terms, the shape of a snailshell, the twist of a horn, the outline of a leaf, the texture of a bone, the fabric of a skeleton, the stream-lines of fish or bird, the fairy lace-work of an insect's wing. Even to do this we must learn from the mathematician to eliminate and to discard; to keep the type in mind and leave the single case, with all its accidents, alone; and to find in this sacrifice of what matters little and conservation of what matters much one of the peculiar excellences of the method of mathematics.

D'Arcy Thompson, *On Growth and Form*[20]

The interested anatomist, surgeon, anthropologist, or embryologist – like the palmist – needs an accurate system of identification for the various parts of the hand; a system that enables each to pinpoint a particular line or area, instantaneously and precisely, without semantic confusion. For the scientist, the romantic nomenclature of the chirologist was obviously quite out of the question. How could he possibly retain the respect of his peers if he had to refer to, say, the Venus mount, the finger of Saturn, or the lines of Fate or Mercury?

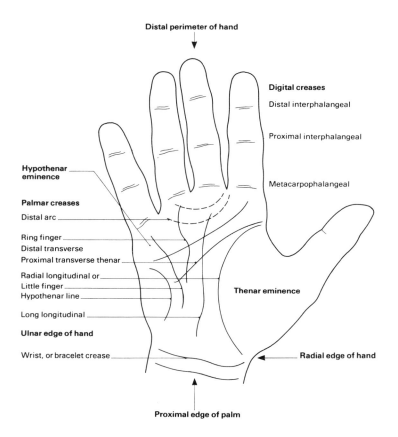

Figure 26   Dermatoglyphic terminology

In the early nineteen hundreds Professor Wood-Jones, whose anatomical speciality was the human hand, introduced a system of terminology which is still, with minor variations, in use today (see Figure 26).
Sadly, to the man in the street, the intelligent and impartial observer, this
may be even more confusing than the language of traditional palmistry,
but abstruse technical jargon is the privilege of the specialist, whatever
his field. It's the 'green door' behind which he can hide, the armour that
shields him from attack.

Although not entirely satisfactory, we'll continue to use chirological

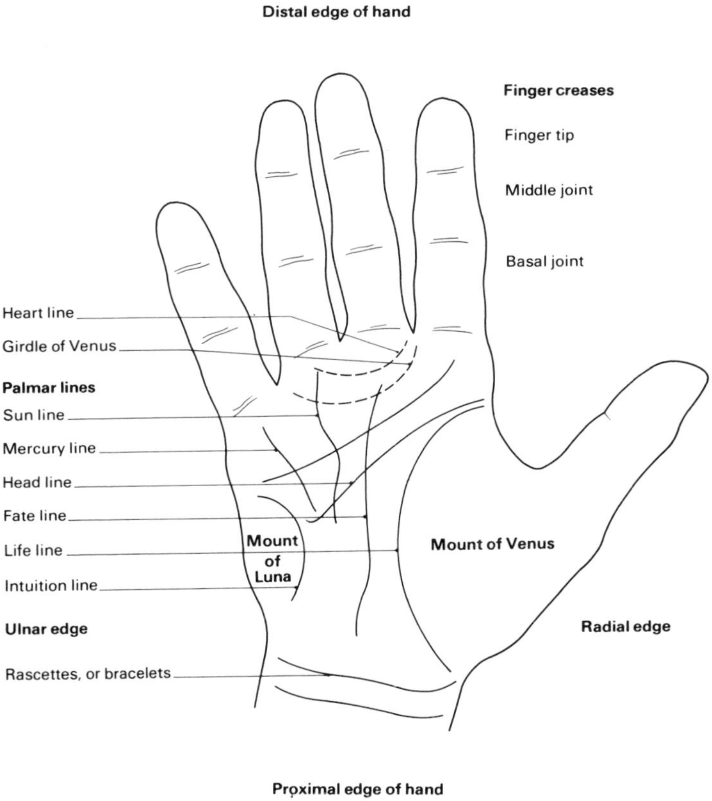

Figure 27   Palmistic terminology

terms in the text that follows (see Figure 27). Even though it still comes under the heading of jargon, I suspect that many of my readers will be more familiar with palmistic than scientific jargon, and there's no doubt that it will be easier to recall! In some cases, these terms do seem to be physiologically appropriate. The 'Heart' line, for instance appears to respond to both emotional states of being, and to the condition of the physical pump, while the 'Head' line does seem to signal confusion, mental illness, head injury or severe headaches. At this stage, we have no idea why there should be any connection between the line and the organ, we only know that – according to repeated chirological studies – there is.

Dr Charlotte Wolff, the psychologist, like most other scientists before and since, takes great pains to dissociate herself from 'quack fortune-tellers'. Into this category, she lumps every hand reader without 'proper' scientifically approved credentials. While admitting that, 'Some of its traditions – those which can be explained on physiological grounds – are valuable', she has 'no hesitation in agreeing that chiromancy . . . does not possess a scientific foundation'. She then goes on to confirm one of the principles fundamental to modern palmistry, namely that it *is* possible to assess an individual's character and his mental and physical health from his hands, and from the palmar 'crease' lines.

It is difficult to understand why medicine, conscious of the correlation between the hand and endocrine disturbance, with its effect on the whole personality, should not have carried the study further, for it seems fairly obvious that links exist between the hand and the endocrine glands. But this step has not been taken by physicians, an omission which precludes the further step of investigating particulars of the hand in connexion with physical and mental disorders in general.

My own researches on the hand in endocrine abnormalities have demonstrated that it can be used as a signpost for diagnosing both the illness itself and its psychological implications.[3]

Sir Francis Galton, in the very first paragraph of his pioneering work, *Finger Prints*, first published in 1892, reveals the same sardonic bias when he opines,

The palms of the hand and the soles of the feet are covered with two totally distinct classes of marks. The most conspicuous are the creases or folds of the skin which interest the followers of palmistry, but which are no more significant to others than the creases in old clothes; they show the lines of most frequent flexure, and nothing more.[7]

Galton's book on the significance of the epidermal lines and ridge patterns is still required reading for the student of dermatoglyphics, though in the ninety years since it was published much more has been learned about the embryological development of the lines and ridges and their significance.

It used to be generally accepted that the lines were no more than 'flexion creases', and a direct result of the way the growing foetus moved its tiny hands and fingers in the womb.

Schaeuble (1933), however, found that the thenar crease was already present in embryos of 27 mm (C–R) length, i.e., at about 7 weeks' gestation. The proximal and distal transverse flexion creases were observed in 40 mm C–R embryos (about 9 weeks' gestation). These observations were confirmed by Würth (1937), who found that the flexion creases develop during the second and third embryonal month.[21]

A few minutes spent flexing your own hand in an attempt to make the skin fold in a direction that corresponds with some of the lines should be more than enough to disprove the flexion crease theory. Of course, the skin on the palm *will* fold along the tracks made by the major lines, but try the same trick with some of the others – those that rise vertically up the palm, or the smaller ones that form the 'stars', circles, and rectangles so beloved of the fortune-teller. You, too, may begin to wonder whether there isn't another explanation for the phenomenon.

The hypothesis currently supported by some hand analysts – that the lines are caused by constant stimulation of the nerve endings – is a little more promising, but again not entirely satisfactory. Beryl Hutchinson surmised that,

as we think in our brains so do the nerves send their tiny impulses to the hand, but they must be excited frequently or dramatically to show and retain the habitual path of thought on the palm.[12]

If this is so, how can we explain the fact that the hands of an undeveloped embryo – obviously incapable at two to three months of experiencing for itself strong feelings or emotions – are already complete with three major lines? At this point its whole existence is geared solely to growth and survival. Recent research, however, does suggest that the embryo may be influenced by the emotional as well as by the physical condition of the mother: logical enough if we accept that chemical and glandular changes are initiated by mood, and this may go some way towards explaining the often quite remarkable similarity between the hands of a new-born baby and those of his mother.

In *The Secret Life of the Unborn Child*, Dr Thomas Verny describes this process:

Physically, just as an unborn child develops in nine months from a tiny undifferentiated speck of protoplasm into a highly defined creature with a complex brain, nervous system, and body, emotionally he grows from an insensate being into one who can register and process very intricate and perplexing feelings and emotions.[22]

As a psychiatrist, Dr Verny is understandably excited by the probability that the formation of the ego starts – not between a child's second and fourth year, as Freud believed – but in the foetus from the fourth month of inter-uterine life onwards, when his nervous system first becomes capable of transmitting sensation to his higher brain centres.

Maternal emotions such as anger, anxiety and fear will . . . prompt furious kicking. A good example of this are those tragic babies Dr Sontag described who suffered because of their mothers' serious stress. In these instances what causes the baby to kick is usually a combination of 'outside' and 'inside' events. The mother's anxiety provoking hormones are flooding his system, making him worried and fearful. Her behaviour and her emotions are also affecting him. Almost anything that upsets her also upsets him, and nearly as quickly. New studies show that within a fraction of a second after fear has set his mother's heart racing, his begins pounding at double his normal rate.[22]

Dr Verny is convinced that the mind and personality of the growing child is shaped by the thoughts and feelings of his mother 'in fundamental ways'. How that mind develops depends 'largely on whether her thoughts and emotions are positive and reinforcing or negative and etched with ambivalence.'

Appropriately enough, the first line to appear, at about seven weeks' gestation, is the Life line (see Figure 29 in Chapter 5). The Head and Heart lines are complete at or around nine weeks after conception,

although he is still so small that he could easily move about inside a goose egg, and weighs only one ounce. By the end of the [third] month he can kick his legs, turn his feet, curl and fan his toes, make a fist, move his thumb, bend his wrist, turn his head, squint, frown, open his mouth and press his lips tightly together.[23]

Spontaneous movement of the tiny hands doesn't normally occur till after the twelfth week, three weeks or so *after* the lines have formed. This was recorded by Schaeuble in 1933 and confirmed by Würth in 1937. Würth therefore concluded that flexion creases developed independently of either palm or finger movements. He found 'no relationship between the embryonal creases and the development of the underlying bones and muscles of the hand.' This was in direct contradiction to the earlier findings of Professor Wood-Jones who, while admitting that the lines, 'do not always, or even generally, mark upon the surface the exact position of the underlying bony joint,' was still adamant that they marked the site of that joint. In Wood-Jones's view, the point of skin movement may be translated some distance from the point of joint movement by the intervention of various tissues. The flexure lines upon well-worn boots or garments do not mark accurately the site of the crease lines upon the skin, for the resistance of the intervening layers of socks and shirts has to be reckoned with. In like manner, the flexure lines upon the skin may not mark the line of the joint, since various layers of muscles, ligaments, etc., may be interposed between the moving bones and the yielding skin.[14]

Another promising theory, and one that isn't necessarily at odds with the findings of Beryl Hutchinson, or Dr Verny, strongly suggests a genetic basis for both the lines and the skin-ridge patterns. The lines – and the characteristics the palmist claims to be able to read from them – seem to be part of our genetic inheritance, transmitted at the moment of conception. We have to remember, though, that at this stage the individual,

exists only in a potential state. He contains the dominant factors responsible for the visible characteristics of his parents. And also the recessive factors, which have remained hidden during their entire life. According to their relative position in the new individual's chromosomes, the recessive factors will manifest their activity or will be neutralized by dominant factors.[1]

What he eventually becomes depends upon the experiences he encounters during the course of his life. Mental and emotional muscles develop in the same way as physical ones do – by being used. Whether or not our potential is activated or remains dormant may appear to be a matter of chance, for we are to an almost incredible degree at the mercy of our environment. How much we, as individuals, are responsible for the unbalanced mess the ecology is in is something else again. A matter we will, sooner or later, have to refer to our consciences as consumers. The fact is that by passive acceptance, if not by active participation, we are all guilty of raping, despoiling and vandalizing our environment, of fouling the only nest we have.

The mental and physical manifestations of this despoliation of our surroundings are every day more apparent in man. It's no longer a matter of conjecture. We are inexorably pushing humankind to the limits of its adaptability and further, into a disintegration that goes beyond mental and physical breakdown. The hands of those who come to consult me are living proof of this. Out of a collection of thousands upon thousands of prints, there are very few I would be able to describe as belonging to healthy, happy, and fulfilled individuals. The irony of it is that we cannot develop as healthy individuals until we learn to live in tune with nature.

The American Indians were instinctively aware of this:

> The old Lakota was wise.
> He knew that man's heart
> away from nature becomes hard;
> he knew that lack of respect
> for growing, living things
> soon led to lack of respect
> for humans too.[24]

In this connection it's interesting to note that one of the best prints in my collection, one of the healthiest, belongs to Dusty Miller. It can be no coincidence that in his chosen work as a 'practitioner in the Old Arts' (he used to be a successful executive), he has a very close relationship with nature. It's a give and take relationship in which an awareness of the rhythms of life plays an integral part. I have no doubt at all that a hand-print taken when Dusty was still part of the rat-race would have had very little in common with this one! (see Figure 28a.)

Richard St Barbe Baker was another totally integrated individual who was in tune with nature. He was known in Africa and worldwide as the 'Man of the Trees'. Up to the limit of his three score years and ten and well into his eighties, St Barbe Baker crusaded for vital reafforestation after felling, protected the giant redwoods from the timber industry, and made the deserts fertile. He had the inner awareness we must all develop to ensure our survival – the awareness:

that we are in a vital and intimate relationship with plant life – that we are ana-tomically dependent on plant life. It is the plant life of this earth that makes oxygen available to us. The depletion of the plant life in cities is a major factor in the cause of frequent and deep states of depression in city dwellers. Both body and psyche are suffering from too much carbon dioxide.[25]

Julius Spier, the psycho chirologist who successfully interested C.G. Jung in the study of hands, was well aware of these various influences, and in particular of their importance during the formative years. After watching Spier at work, Jung commented that 'the results he has achieved have made a lasting impression on me'.

Modern science increasingly relinquishes the medieval conception of the separateness of body and mind, and just as the body in the view of science is neither something mechanical nor chemical, so the mind seems to be but another aspect of the living body.[26]

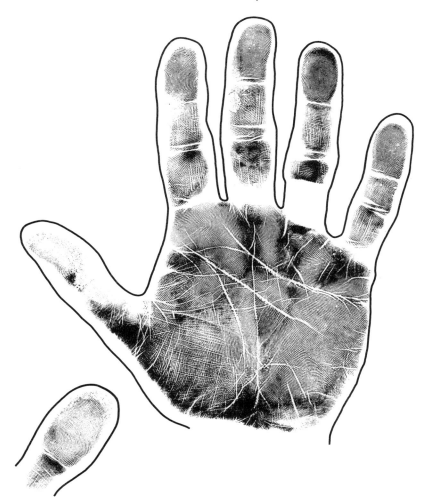

Figure 28a

An individual enjoying a symbiotic relationship with his environment has hands that reflect equilibrium of mind, body, and spirit. For the majority, such an idyllic state of affairs is quite out of reach, and their hands show the resulting imbalance. The lines proliferate or fade away, become thicker or thinner, faded, broken, islanded, or otherwise dis-

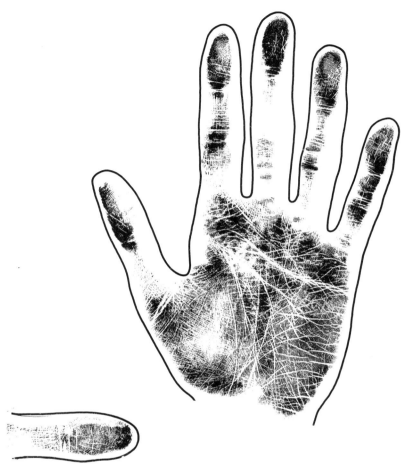

Figure 28b

turbed (see Figure 28b). Spier held that much of the blame for this could be laid at our father's door, but since we're all our parents' children, we're left with the classical chicken and egg conundrum to solve before we can proceed any further. Adam and Eve have a lot to answer for!

So many parents never become what they should have become, and unconscious of this fact, try to find the fulfilment of their own frustrated wishes in their child without realizing they are continuing the vicious circle which now prevents their own child from finding the fulfilment of its true possibilities and talents. Here the analysis of the hand offers a unique possibility of solving both difficulties: to ascertain the disposition of the parents, and particularly that part of the disposition with which the child is directly, biologically and physically, connected, and the individual disposition of the child.[10]

If we could only, Spier felt, 'know' ourselves fully, and then our children, our psychological health would undoubtedly improve beyond recognition, but 'how difficult and hard it is to become what we essentially are'.

Noel Jaquin's researches convinced him that,

each line and mark in the human hand is formed by some mental or physical attribute, there is not the slightest doubt. It is equally certain that our knowledge of the significance of these lines has steadily progressed, till today, not only does a man's character stand clearly revealed by his hands, but his health – past, present and to come – are there to be read by all who have the requisite skill and knowledge.[13]

Jaquin devoted over fifty years of his life to chirological researches and like the psychologist Charlotte Wolff, had no doubt that the lines resulted from conscious and unconscious mental processes, and that – in as far as our 'future' is dependant on deeply entrenched attitudes – it is possible to forecast *trends* in both health and lifestyle. He was always at pains, however, to explain that, in his view, the hand only:

indicates the trend of the life and if this trend is unfavourable, then some very definite cause can be found either in the circumstances surrounding the life of the individual or in the individual himself. Thus, it is open to correction and consequent improvement.[13]

Wolff held that the crease lines on the palmar surface were not nearly as important as the shape and form of the hand in general, and that any consideration of those lines in relation to an individual's psyche had to take account of both aspects. The psychologist observed that,

The more frequent and complex [. . .] a person's nervous and emotional stimuli, the more will emotional tension and nervousness be produced in him, and this will affect the scale and variety of his involuntary movements and gestures and will be registered in the accessory crease-lines of the palm. We have, therefore, a correlation between the number of the accessory crease-lines and the nervous make-up . . .[3]

She found proof of this in the prints she took of the hands of boxers, wrestlers, 'feeble-minded persons and high-grade imbeciles'. Here there were the minimum of accessory creases (see Figure 28c). In her analysis of the hands of 1,600 right-handed subjects Wolff found more accessory crease lines in the left. This ties in with the old chirological belief that the left hand is linked with our unconscious, with emotional, spiritual, intuitive and creative awareness.

Figure 28c

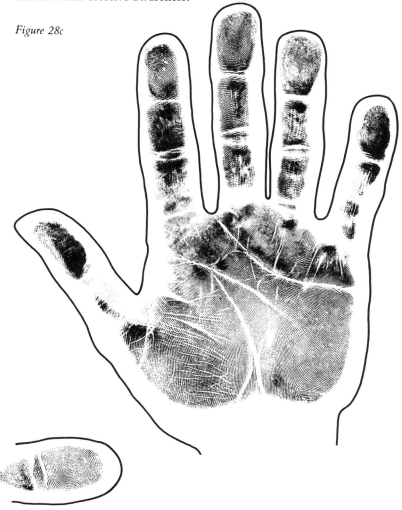

In a similar survey of 2,000 people, including examples of 'every social class', 78 per cent proved to have more crease lines on the left hand. Overall, Wolff found the left hand 'more revealing of the deeper-seated emotions and therefore of the subject's difficulties and conflicts'.

Despite her avowed contempt for palmists and fortune tellers – and she admitted to seeing very little difference between them – Dr Wolff was at least prepared to make an independent investigation into the possible meaning of the lines of the hand. Surprisingly, the results she got coincided with much that palmists had been saying for years, though the psychologist wasn't generous enough to allow that there might, just might, be one or two palmists capable of bringing a scientific approach to their art. Presumably they had stumbled on these truths by a happy accident!

Most – if not all – of the scientists involved in dermatoglyphic research today seem to follow the lead, given in 1892, of Francis Galton. They tend to concentrate on the skin-ridge patterns as possible significators of disease, using the lines merely to mark the boundaries between one part of the hand and another. A few grudgingly allow that,

Strictly speaking, the study of flexion creases is not a part of the study of dermatoglyphics, but the two are closely allied. Irregularities in ridge alignment often occur in the primary creases. Abnormal flexion creases are found in some pathological conditions and may be characteristic.[27]

It is surely more than a little strange – one might even say unscientific – to pay such scant attention to the lines of the hands. After all, the three primary lines are completely formed in the nine-week-old foetus, while the palmar ridge patterns,

are completed only after the sixth prenatal month, when the glandular folds are fully formed and after the sweat gland secretion and keratinization have begun.[27]

That is, when the foetus is fourteen weeks old. The embryo is in a very real sense much more plastic and malleable during these early weeks, and especially vulnerable to toxins and pollutants up to the end of the first three months. A potentially healthy infant exposed to rubella, certain drugs, or combinations of drugs (thalidomide, diethylstilbestrol), at a crucial moment in the womb is in danger of developing abnormalities. Even fluoride has recently come under suspicion as a factor in the incidence of Down's syndrome.

In general the effects of exposure are likely to be more severe in early prenatal life when tissue growth is at a maximum rate, and the opportunity for interference with the complex sequence of events leading to cell division and differentiation are obviously greatest.[28]

In the circumstances it's illogical to assume that only the ridged skin would be disturbed by these abnormalities, yet the early dermatoglyphicists, led by Cummins and Midlo, relegated the lines to an inferior position as 'anatomical landmarks', significant merely 'because of peculiarities of epidermal ridges coursing in them. The flexion creases of the palm are the ' "lines" of the palmist'.

Why should it be taken as read that it is the lines that disturb the skin ridges? We know that the lines develop first. Had it not been for the long-standing bias against palmists, I'm quite sure that Galton, Cummins and Midlo and their peers would have adopted a more scientific (i.e., rational) than emotional approach to the study and interpretation of the so-called crease lines. Dismissing them as lines of flexure is too easy. If it were really that simple we'd expect to find remarkable similarities in the angle and setting of the lines, especially in hands of similar shape and size. Though there *are* often similarities the percentage of cases showing measurable differences is too great, even in those doing the same work.

It's an ironical fact that the sort of palmist who has given palmistry such a bad name in scientific quarters doesn't even pretend to be scientific in his, or more often her, approach. This breed of seers would do as well, or better, with crystal ball or Tarot cards, leaving the field free for hand analysts of the calibre of Spier, Jaquin, Debrunner, and Hutchinson. Unfortunately, scientific resistance to reading any significance into the lines of the hands seems deeply and permanently entrenched despite the efforts of these pioneers to rebuild palmistry to scientifically tenable specifications. Dermatoglyphic researchers prefer to restrict themselves to the only slightly less controversial field of epidermal ridge patterns. As Herbert Spencer remarked, 'There is a principle which is a bar against all information, which is proof against all argument, and which cannot fail to keep a man in everlasting ignorance. That principle is condemnation before investigation.'[29]

5

The Physiology and Embryogenesis of the Skin-Ridge Patterns

The skin on the fingertips and palmar and plantar surfaces of man is not smooth. It is grooved by curious ridges, which form a variety of configurations. These configurations have attracted the attention of laymen for millenia. They have also evoked the serious interest of scientists for more than three centuries. The anatomist Bidloo provided a description of ridge detail in the seventeenth century. Since then, additional information has been added by anthropologists, biologists, and geneticists. For the last century, the fact that each individual's ridge configurations are unique has been utilized as a means of personal identification especially by law enforcement officials. Widespread medical interest in epidermal ridges developed only in the last several decades when it became apparent that many patients with chromosomal aberrations had unusual ridge formations. Inspection of skin ridges, therefore, promised to provide a simple, inexpensive means for determining whether a given patient had a particular chromosomal defect.

Schaumann and Alter, *Dermatoglyphics in Medical Disorders*,[21]

We know that the skin has several important functions to fulfil. It's designed to keep out the water, wind and weather and to keep in, and in good shape, blood vessels, organs and other working parts. As a result of sweating or forming 'goose bumps' a stable temperature can be maintained.

The skin surface of the human hand, far from being smooth and alabaster, as so often in romantic novels, is neither smooth nor white but highly textured and multi-coloured. It is deeply etched with lines, grooves, folds and furrows and studded with pits for hairs and open ducts for the excretion of sweat. In living hands veins show blue, arteries show pink and for good measure freckles and 'liver spots' show brown; only dead hands are lily-white.[17]

Highly magnified under the electron microscope, the skin is seen to be as densely populated as any capital city. Micro-organisms, friendly and some not so friendly, live and work, reproduce and die there amongst the rolling hills and valleys of the body's superstratum. Under the scrutiny of the naked eye, the skin of palms and soles is found to be of a different texture: not smooth as elsewhere in the body, with the finger tips particularly liable to cómplex configurations of ridged skin. Why should this be, and what purpose, if any, do these minute corrugations serve?

The ridges may be fine and numerous, or wider and coarser, so at this stage it might be useful to beg, borrow, or buy a magnifying glass and to take a good look at these patterns on your own hands. For most of us, the skin on the soles of our feet isn't quite as accessible, though it can be just as interesting!

The epidermis, or that part of the skin that we can see, is actually several layers thick. The topmost layer of dead, keratinous cells is constantly flaking away and being replaced from below by new cells that have worked their way gradually to the surface for this very purpose. The process continues from birth to death, a rhythmic tide of erosion and replacement, replacement and erosion. The ridges and patterns on palms and soles (in scientific parlance, the palmar and plantar surfaces) have been exercising pragmatic minds for at least 300 years, and the manner in which they form, their purpose and meaning, raise questions which continue to tax the intelligence of biologists, physiologists, anthropologists and other scientists the world over.

Since it was discovered that chromosomal abnormalities are frequently accompanied by unusual ridge patterns, there has been a fresh upsurge of interest in the study of these peculiar patterns, designated dermatoglyphics by Cummins and Midlo in 1926. In the last ten to fifteen years, the power of the electron microscope has been brought to bear on the

Figure 29   The hands grow from a 'plate' with finger ridges in the fifth (1) and sixth weeks (2). In the seventh and eighth weeks (3) fingers, thumbs, and fingerprints form. The prominent touch pads regress in the third month (4).

The feet follow the hands and begin in the sixth week (5), and forty-eight hours later (6) have larger toe ridges. The heel appears by the end of the sixth week (7) and grows out in the next five days (8). The prominent walking pads regress in the third month (9)

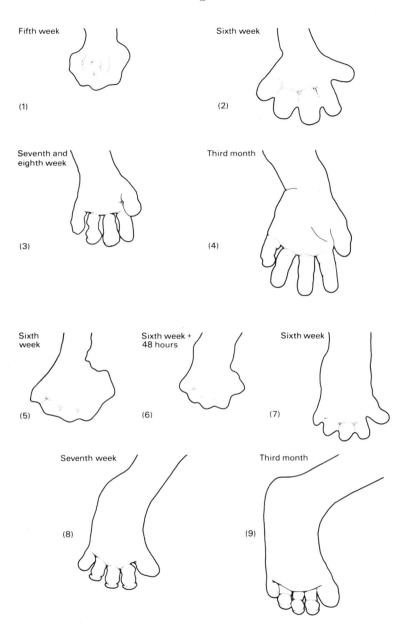

Fifth week

(1)

Sixth week

(2)

Seventh and eighth week

(3)

Third month

(4)

Sixth week

(5)

Sixth week + 48 hours

(6)

Sixth week

(7)

Seventh week

(8)

Third month

(9)

problem, with Hirsch and Schweichel (1971 and 1973), and Penrose and Ohara (1973) specializing in the pre-natal development of epidermal ridges. Obviously, before disturbances can be accurately pinpointed it's necessary to have a full understanding of normal developmental mechanisms.

It is now known that these ridges start to appear in the foetus at around the fourth month, or when the hand is 3.5 mm or so long. The process is completed in the six-month-old foetus when the hand has grown to approximately 15.5 mm. There appears to be a connection between the size and shape of the volar pads that appear on the fingertips, finger-bases and sometimes the middle of the palm, and the type of pattern that emerges.

The formation of these pads is first visible on the fingertips in the sixth to seventh week of embryonic development. The pads become very prominent during the subsequent several weeks, diminish again in the fifth month, and dis-appear completely in the sixth month. Within this period the dermal ridges coalesce into specific patterns, replacing the volar pads.[21]

The ridges on the soles of the feet form in the same way, but two or three weeks later and are, in general, far less complex arrangements than those on the palms (see Figure 29).

Figure 30a   Diagrammatic representation of ridged skin

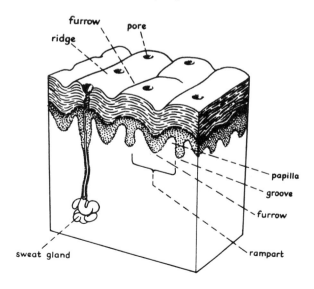

A fully-formed section of ridged skin would look something like Figure 30a. The ridges are studded at more or less regular intervals with minute pores – the ducts along which the sweat glands propel their secretions to the surface. These sweat, or eccrine, glands are found all over the body but in far greater concentration in the palms of the hands and soles of the feet. Lubrication here facilitates gripping and grasping, and enhances the sense of touch by causing the papillary ridges to swell and stand proud, thus making them more effective contact points. According to Professor Napier, the eccrine glands in the hands are especially interesting, since:

they have a slightly different developmental history; furthermore, they cease activity during sleep and they respond not to *thermal* but to psychic stimuli under stress, a function believed to be mediated by hormones.[17]

Each ridge is formed over a glandular fold, and each furrow corresponds to a furrow fold in the *stratum germinativum.*

There seems to be tremendous variation in the dimensions of these ridges from person to person, and though there is a loose correlation between ridge width and body size, there's no absolute rule. Patterns tend to cover a larger area, and ridges to be coarser in the right hands of right-handed people but once again it's impossible to be dogmatic. A pity because it would be useful, especially in forensic science, to be able to tell an individual's sex or racial group from a palm or sole print, but it can't be done. Professor Harold Cummins' early work suggested a basis for linking ridge size with two specific genetically controlled mechanisms – one related to body size generally, which modified the action of an independent factor controlling ridge width. Recent studies confirm that heredity plays a vital role in the form that the ridges on palms and soles take. It's been known for many years that, though ridge patterns seem alike at first sight, they are never identical. Children inherit not only traits, mannerisms, and physical characteristics from their parents, but common ridge and line formations too. Indeed,

It would be surprising if the traits of dermatoglyphics were not inherited, since there is reason to expect that dermatoglyphics are subject to the same biological laws which determine inheritance of other characteristics, whether structural, physiological or psychological. No student of inheritance, however, has claimed that the totality of pattern characteristics is transmitted. The studies have disclosed only transmission of grades of resemblance which invariably fall short of complete likeness.[5]

A study by Gerald Fox, of London's Birkbeck College (1974), suggesting strong links between certain types of fingerprint patterns and personality traits, tends to confirm this. Though this sample was a small one – only 100 subjects – and needs to be repeated with larger groups of people, Mr Fox proved to his own satisfaction that there was ample evidence to support his theory, which was that an individual's genetic make-up may influence, not just his physique, but also his personality. 'In other words, the genes that determine aspects of our character also form the patterns of our skin-prints.'

It's remarkable but true that of all the teeming millions alive today, and the millions that have gone before, no two handprints have ever been duplicated. Even in monozygotic, that is to say identical, twins the same rule applies – be they ever so minute there are always subtle differences in the palmar patterns that make it impossible to mistake the prints of one for the other. Should cloning ever become a viable proposition one would assume that each replica would be indistinguishable in every respect – including his hand prints – from the original. A fascinating thought, but somehow I hope I'm not going to be around to find out!

The principle that ridge patterns can be inherited is well established even if the actual mode of transmission is not clear, and analysis of the fingerprint patterns as a means of establishing paternity in disputed cases was mooted in the early twentieth century. It lost the little support it had gained when it was found to have similar disadvantages to blood tests carried out for the same reason. The evidence only proved useful in those cases in which rare and unusual ridge patterns (or blood groups) were passed on, and though sometimes a possibility could be excluded, dermatoglyphics weren't able to prove paternity outright.

A multiplicity of theories have been put forward to try and explain the development of specific ridge formations in the individual or to prove that these are no more than random phenomena. Though most authorities do acknowledge that heredity has a strong influence on pattern formation, there's argument about the degree to which patterns evolving in the embryo can actually be modified by environmental factors. It's well known that the first weeks of pregnancy – those when the new mother-to-be may be quite unaware of her status – are extremely hazardous due to the rapid rate of cell division. At this stage, many common drugs (including aspirin) and exposure to such viral infections as rubella can and do cause damage. Even if there is no overt or visible effect, it seems that postnatal dermatoglyphic analysis can be a 'sensitive indicator of even subtle inter-uterine rubella damage'.[21]

It has been suggested that dermal ridge configurations are dictated by physical and topographical influences in much the same way as volcanic lava, which forms patterns as it settles and hardens. Remarkably similar patterns occur in windblown desert sand and sands on the beach after the tide has gone out, a fact first noted by Cummins and Midlo in the 1920s (see Figure 30b). Some workers believe the ridges always follow the lines

Figure 30b   Photograph of a sand dune showing similar ridge phenomena . . .

Figure 30c   . . . as does the zebra's ridge-patterned hide

of greatest convexity in the embryonic epidermis, others that they're linked with the underlying arrangement of nerves. Hirsch and Schweichel (1973) point to,

the regularity in the arrangement of the blood vessel-nerve pairs under the smooth epidermis-corium border which exists shortly before formation of the glandular folds. They postulated that the folds are induced by the vessel-nerve pairs.[21]

Whatever mechanism is responsible, the permanent character of the skin-ridge patterns has been known for centuries with hand- or fingerprints being used as marks of personal identity in many different cultures, Ancient Egyptian, Indian, and Japanese among them. Eastern palmists working today refer to not merely the lines but the skin ridges when making their prognostications, further enriching their readings by applying the principles of the *I Ching* as they've done for hundreds of years.

In the past, the medical researcher has tended to favour programmes investigating a possible connection between the growth of specific skin-ridge patterns and inherited disorders and malformations. By and large, he seems to have ignored, or been unaware of, the fact that ailments of a more transitory nature – such as mental depression, colitis, cystitis, fibrositis, some heart conditions, and many more common afflictions, are also heralded in the hands in the form of degeneration of ridges and lines (see Figure 31).

Noel Jaquin, Beryl Hutchinson, Julius Spier, and other eminent chiro-logists devoted their lives to building a scientific base for palmistry and proved beyond any reasonable doubt that, not only do the lines and ridges degenerate under stress, they also repair themselves when the cause of the stress is removed. The Society for the Study of Physiological Patterns, founded by Jaquin in 1945, continues to pursue those aims.

There is a major difference in approach here, and it appears unlikely that the twain shall ever meet. While the scientist *per se* tries valiantly to reduce all his findings to the lowest common denominator, the scientific hand analyst, by virtue of his chirological background, remains aware at all times of the unique character of each and every print he takes. He, too, has recourse to common denominators – there have to be some ground rules – but he's also on the alert for the differences between one man's hands and the next. His training tells him that these consistently repre-sent specific differences in personality. Looking for similarities is a useful device, but it does have limitations. Mr and Mrs Average and their family (of opinion poll renown) are never representative of real flesh and blood people!

Central to both science and chirology is a tradition of meticulous observation, and the modern palmist believes that,

the patterns formed by the papillary ridges and furrows show the basic attitude to life which will colour all the potential as shown by the shape, and by the use that is being made of that potential as indicated by the lines.[12]

The research scientist builds his case for the use of dermatoglyphics in medical diagnosis and prognosis (and the police for their system of iden-

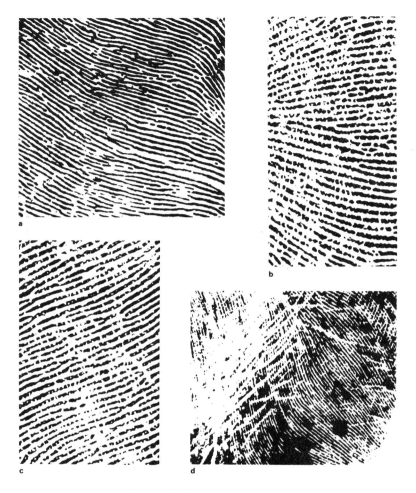

Figure 31   a, a micro-photograph of an imprint of a healthy hand, showing normal clear ridge lines.

b, a micro-photograph of an imprint of palmar skin, showing the typical malformation of the ridge pattern in the case of an acute bacterial infection of the intestine.

c, a micro-photograph of a portion of an imprint of the hand of a man suffering from malaria. Observe the minute white dots in the ridge lines.

d, a number of fine lines running slantwise down the hand indicate gastric disorder and acidity of the digestive tract, generally the result of faulty feeding tification) on the permanence of and similarity between patterns in different individuals – permanent in that once established in a normally healthy person, the arrangement of these patterns on palms and soles doesn't alter in the slightest detail from birth to death.

Cases have been recorded of desperate criminals undergoing painful plastic surgery in vain attempts to eradicate the ridge patterns, or mutilate them beyond recognition. Even in those instances where the patterns *were* obliterated the 'advantage' was short-lived. They failed to take into account the fact that their hands would still show unique patterns of scarring – in their own way just as distinctive as the 'dabs' previously on record!

Ill health, burns, or contact with chemicals may cause the skin ridges to disintegrate or atrophy, but invariably, when health is restored (unless the nerve supply has been damaged irretrievably) the pattern is also restored. Should a child under the age of twelve or so have the misfortune to lose the tip of a finger accidentally, plastic surgeons have discovered that, provided the finger hasn't been severed below the first joint, the entire tip, complete with pattern indistinguishable from the original and the entire finger nail, will regenerate within a very short space of time. No attention, apart from simple dressings and ensuring that the wound stays clean, is necessary in most cases.

It is in the relative stability of the skin ridges and lines on human palms and soles that the future of medical palmistry as a barometer of health lies. If the body *is* equipped with its very own early warning system, and the unique marks we bear on our hands and feet *can* indicate a tendency to fall prey to a specific disease or ailment, the implications for medicine are nothing short of revolutionary. How ironic if the sophisticated and prohibitively expensive machinery without which hospitals, clinics, and surgeries nowadays can't seem to function (and which ensures that treatment is out of reach for the majority of National Health Service dependent patients) should prove finally to be inferior to the human hand!

There must be thousands of genetically determined diseases in existence, and many geneticists hold that *every* disease is caused or influenced in some way by genetic mechanisms. Three out of every hundred babies are born with major birth defects and more than 5 per cent of all the children admitted to hospital in Great Britain are suffering from a disorder which is entirely genetic in origin. Approximately 10 per cent of the entire population has, or will develop at some time in their lives, a disorder that has been transmitted via faulty gene stock.

Whether or not we are agreed that all our ills are genetically ordained is immaterial. In recent years German and American teams have been successfully identifying diseases – not only actual but latent – by analysing the skin-ridge patterns of their subjects. West German researchers have claimed an 80 per cent success rate in predicting a new-born baby's chances of developing such illnesses as heart or kidney disease, cancer, leukaemia, diabetes and other glandular malfunctions. The Americans have reported similar results.

Researchers have so far concentrated almost exclusively on the apparent link between chromosomal abnormalities and specific derma-toglyphs, presumably because these signs are immutable in form, though the physical condition of the skin can and does vary tremendously in the normal individual, reflecting his general fitness and well-being. Unfor-tunately, for the dermatoglyphic researcher to prove his point, a high percentage of the subjects he's studying have of necessity to fall ill. It doesn't help his case much if several of those subjects spontaneously regain their health for no apparent reason – unless of course he can demonstrate that a particular course of treatment was responsible and that there was a corresponding improvement in the condition of the skin ridges. Or that the environmental conditions predisposing a subject to breakdown have abated, again allowing regeneration to occur.

From my own limited researches into the hand and health I have con-firmed that well-being is dependent on the mental, physical, spiritual and social integration of the individual. The internal milieu is just as impor-tant as the external. A man's latent potential is at the mercy of the che-mical and the psychological climate in which he was reared, and on his early emotional conditioning. Favourable conditions, though,

cannot transform a weak, apathetic, dispersed, timid, inactive child into an energetic man, a powerful and audacious leader. Vitality, imagination, boldness are never entirely due to environment. Neither can they be repressed by it.[1]

The palmist has long believed the hand capable of signalling inherent character, talents, strengths and weaknesses. Now, thanks to derma-toglyphic research, early diagnosis of health breakdown can be added to the list.

6

The Genetic Influence

Am I not unique and possessed of a particular destiny? Yes, up to a point, but the life of even the greatest of individuals is short, and posterity is totally confused with that of one's mate. My children are only half me, and my grandchildren no more than twenty-five per cent. The best I can hope for is a large number of descendants, each of whom bears a tiny portion of me and equally tiny parts of a great many other people. There is no future for an individual. We are just fleeting things. Even our chromosomes, the hand we have been dealt and of which we are so inordinately proud, are evanescent. They get shuffled into oblivion with each new deal. Only the cards themselves remain unchanged. The cards are the genes, and the genes are forever.

Lyall Watson, *Lifetide*[30]

Man is an explorer. He has risked his life discovering new continents, charting the savage polar wastes, conquering the highest mountain ranges and plumbing the deepest ocean depths. The same insatiable search for knowledge that took him to the moon and back – and his artefacts to the farthest reaches of our solar system – has also been focused on the intricate workings of his own body. First on outer, then inner space: the macrocosm, then the microcosm. Few of his adventures have been as enthralling, or as frustrating, with each revelation provoking more questions than it answers.

The laws of heredity tend to be taken for granted nowadays, at least by those outside genetic research laboratories. What exactly is it that is passed on? We've touched on the subject of genetics in previous chapters because it is so closely bound up with what the palmist and the dermatoglyphicist claim to be able to see in our palms and soles. Genetics is the scientific study of heredity, and especially of inherited characteristics and their variegation. Founded on the work of the monk Gregor Mendel, who in 1865 formulated the basic laws of inheritance, it has made its greatest advances since the 1950s. Although it had already been established that the code of life was passed on in the chromosomes, it wasn't till the discovery in 1953 of the molecular structure of DNA (the nucleic acid responsible for transmitting the code) that the science really got off the ground.

All human cells – with the exception of red blood cells – have a nucleus within which resides the genetic material, i.e. chromosomes. Different species are characterized by different numbers of these. A normal human cell has forty-six; twenty-two matched pairs, called autosomes, and two sex chromosomes, each of which can be distinguished from the others by its size and even more accurately,

by using new staining techniques which make it possible to distinguish horizontal bands on every chromosome. Indeed, it seems likely that, *as with our fingerprints*, the banding pattern along each chromosome is unique for each individual person.[19] (our italics)

The chromosomes are, in their turn, made up of genes of which there may be up to several million in any one cell.

It is the gene that is the actual unit of heredity and single genes are so small that they can't be seen, except by the most modern and sophisticated instruments. Each gene corresponds to a particular sequence of the genetic code and both transmits and receives information about protein synthesis and enzyme manufacture. In this way, the genes control all our vital processes. The degree to which we can maintain cell health exactly parallels our general state of well-being. And this, as we've seen, seems to be reflected in the skin-ridge patterns of palms and soles.

We may be lucky enough to inherit a sound constitution, or we may have, or later develop, a genetically influenced condition. Common examples are heart disease, diabetes, high blood pressure, cancer and even a predisposition to allergies. Of the normal complement of forty-six chromosomes, half are derived from the ovum, and half from the sperm. It is from a lottery such as this that each of us in all his miraculous uniqueness emerges. In approximately forty weeks, or 260 days, the zygote divides and continues to duplicate itself until the original cell has topped two million, and is ready to start an independent existence.

To what degree can the environment into which the child is born affect his mental and physical development? Here's where the argument usually starts, with specialists ranged on opposite sides. The geneticist's training encourages him to think heredity imposes itself on the individual in such a way that there's little or nothing he can do to escape its influence. In the psychologist's opinion, virtually any response can be conditioned, provided the stimuli are powerful enough to overcome entrenched attitudes and inclinations.

Research studies have been carried out on identical twins, successfully 'proving' both these theories correct. It seems that of twins parted early in life and allowed to develop independently to adulthood, monozygotic twins will have much more in common with each other than fraternal, or dizygotic, twins who are no more alike than other siblings would be. Some quite remarkable correspondences in both handprints and lines have been recorded. Identical twins have married at the same time, to partners with the same name, producing children within hours of one another, and giving Christian names of remarkable similarity or exactitude.

There are two stages at which the original conceptus can split to give identical twins:

The first occurs very soon after fertilization, at the time when the blastomeres are still totipotent (i.e. potentially capable of giving rise to a complete individual, together with a complete set of supporting membranes, if they should become separated). Thus separation at the two-celled stage would give rise to two viable conceptuses, which would implant independently of each other . . .

The second opportunity for monozygotic twinning arises after implantation and involves only the cells of the inner cell mass. This subdivision . . . implies that each of the groups of cells formed in this way retains sufficient potential to produce a complete embryonic body. As a consequence of this mode of twinning, the two individuals share a single chorion and placenta and may even lie within a single amniotic cavity.[31]

It is at the second stage, incidentally, that conjoined (or 'Siamese') twins can appear as a result of incomplete splitting of the inner cell mass.

Palmists and geneticists won't be surprised to find that,

A high degree of similarity of dermatoglyphic traits has been found between monozygotic twins, whereas considerably less agreement exists between dizygotic twins. These observations have been utilized diagnostically in determining zygosity of twins.[21]

A variety of twin studies in a number of countries add weight to these findings. As they grow older, identical twins tend statistically to reflect more parallels in lifestyle, personality, and disease patterns. Spurts and lags in development aren't nearly as close in fraternal twins. The results of a comparative study of 374 sets of twins between the ages of three months and six years are reproduced in Figure 32 in graph form. These cycles are now thought to be genetically stimulated.

Identical twins 'went up and down in their abilities together' and the profiles of these pairs were much more alike than fraternals.

if one twin lagged in a particular test, so did his or her co-twin; when there was a spurt, it affected both. The same was not true, at least to anywhere near the same extent, among DZ twins, as the graphs also show.[32]

We find, then, that mental development runs parallel in the twins sharing greater genetic resemblance. Identical twins usually have stronger emotional links, too. The hand analyst has for many years claimed the ability to assess character and potential in this way, but because he had no scientifically acceptable proof to present he has tended to be judged a rogue and confidence trickster.

Strictly speaking, of course, the term 'identical' cannot be applied to any human being, twins included. We are all, without exception, individuals, and uniquely different from anyone else. No two *hands* are ever alike, let alone a pair, yet evidence suggesting that certain ridge patterns can be passed on genetically has been piling up for the last 70 years or so. With the exception of one or two dissenters, the majority are agreed that pattern type can be inherited and, though the exact mechanics of transmission aren't known (there's argument as to the role of recessive and dominant genes in the process), ridge configurations remain consistently similar in all identical twin studies. The claim was made (Meyer-Heydenhagen, 1934) that in cases of doubt 90 per cent of monozygotic twins 'could be diagnosed by their palmar dermatoglyphics alone'. Studies carried out since confirm this and take account of both palmar and plantar patterns.

The fact that twins, and siblings to a lesser degree, tend to resemble one another not only in appearance, but also in psychology, intellect, and mental and physical health isn't at all remarkable to the trained hand analyst who has compared their handprints. The scientist and researcher, probably because he has been taught to adopt a blinkered approach to his speciality, whatever it may be, doesn't find it so easy.

the growth of the behavioural sciences in the 1950s and 1960s carried with it the firm conviction that the environment is mainly responsible for shaping psychological and medical development. Intelligence, personality, mental health and illness, not to mention physical health and illness, were seen as owing most to the quality of mothers, the quality of schools, the quality of housing and so on. Lately, however, doubts have grown. These factors remain important . . . but many scientists now suspect that genes play a much bigger part in our lives. And genes may affect our psychological as much as our physical make-up.[32]

Figure 32   Spurts and lags in the mental development of twins. Not only are the monozygotic curves closer than the dizygotic curves but spurts and lags are very similar too

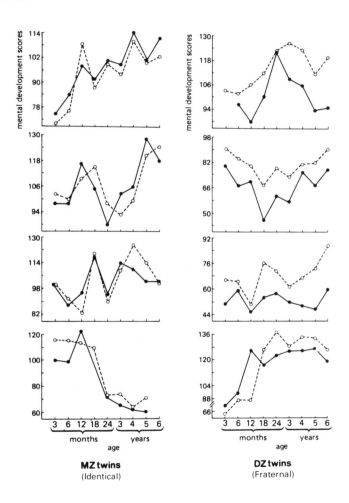

MZ twins
(Identical)

DZ twins
(Fraternal)

If the lines and skin-ridge patterns *are* indeed representative of our genetic inheritance – and our genetic inheritance determines the kind of person we become and the ills to which we're heir, why shouldn't we be able to find in these same patterns clues to both character and health potential? This concept is illustrated in Figure 33.

Arguments about the comparative effect of nature or nurture on an individual strike me as superfluous; every single one of us – and a goodly proportion of our genes – is modified by life and our environment, and our environment cannot fail to be modified by our existence, since we live in a symbiotic relationship with it. It isn't inconceivable that one day soon geneticists will, as a matter of routine, by taking just one cell from each embryo, analyse its complete potential – mental, physical, emotional, and spiritual – picking out areas of weakness suitable for genetic engineering.

Many of us are programmed by our inheritance to react to environmental agents such as antibiotics, and even aspirin, in possibly fatal

Figure 33

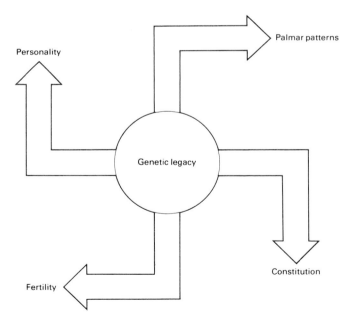

ways. An important enzyme may be missing, so that the drug – or allergen – causes anaphylactic shock. Certain racial groups are more prone than others to such enzyme deficiencies. Experience has taught pharmacologists to take account of these racial variations to drug treatment. Isoniazid, for instance, a drug used in the treatment of tuberculosis, is metabolized more slowly in 5 per cent of Eskimos, 15 per cent of Chinese, 45 per cent of Europeans, and 60 per cent of Asian Indians. This, of course, increases the risk of adverse reactions in the patient. It may cause mental disturbance, numbness, fever, rashes, swollen glands, and raised blood pressure and is contra-indicated in pregnant women.

The main force of dermatoglyphic research was directed towards patients with known chromosomal defects as soon as it became apparent that unusual ridge formations often accompanied such defects. A vast body of knowledge has accumulated over the last fifty years or so, but it was Sir Francis Galton (1822–1916) who led the way by pioneering 'fundamental fingerprint studies concerned with morphology, classification, inheritance and racial variation'.

Galton's interest in heredity focused during his later years on the possibility that its principles could usefully be applied to raising mental and physical standards in the population as a whole. He believed that his fingerprint studies might prove of value in this work. In 1883, he coined the term 'Eugenics' to cover it. In 1904, the Eugenics Record Office was set up in London, and in 1933 the University of London gave official recognition to the Francis Galton Laboratory which is nowadays concerned primarily with collecting any relevant data about heredity, and with the detection and possible elimination of such chromosomal disorders as Down's syndrome.

Very little dermatoglyphic research was carried out by the Galton Laboratory after Galton died until 1945, when Professor L.S. Penrose was appointed to the Chair of Eugenics. Just before his appointment his attention was drawn to the work being done in the field by Cummins and Midlo, whose book *Fingerprints, Palms and Soles* had been published two years earlier. One of Professor Penrose's first projects was to set up his own study group, comparing the prints of a control group with those of Down's syndrome victims (see Penrose's *Outline of Human Genetics*, 1963, and *Biology of Mental Defect*, 1964).

Later, in 1959, after it had been shown that mongolism was due to chromosomal abnormality, the study of the finger, palm, and sole prints of persons with other aberrant chromosomes was begun, including comparisons with normal controls.

The work of Professor Penrose and Dr Sarah B. Holt, also of the Galton Laboratory, has done much to turn the tide, making the science of dermatoglyphics respectable in scientific circles. As Dr Holt says in her book *The Genetics of Dermal Ridges*, 'The subject is beginning to play an increasingly important part in human genetics, largely due to its value in the study of chromosomal aberrations.' As such it holds interest not only for geneticists, and cytogeneticists, but also for biologists, paediatricians and anthropologists.

One of the most important roles for dermatoglyphics in the future will be in prenatal screening and genetic counselling. The process of natural selection discovered by Galton's cousin, Charles Darwin, favours the survival of the fit at the expense of the weak and incapacitated. Today we shortcircuit that process by protecting the weak and the mentally and physically disabled, and encouraging them to have children.

The average man of tomorrow will, if things continue in the present style, be far less strong, skilful and able. Today, through our medical skills, we encourage the survival of genes which would have been self-limiting a few centuries ago.[33]

More than 3000 genetic diseases have been identified, and many more are genetically influenced, but the more capable we become of saving children with such problems, the more trouble we're storing up. It has been estimated that by the early twenty-first century social and medical resources will be stretched to breaking point by the geriatric load which is expected then. Multiply the number of aged by a factor of X, representing the extrapolated number of mentally and physically handicapped existing now, and you have a recipe for disaster. Yet if only half the resources now spent on providing technological crutches for these people were invested in research designed to identify and eliminate the causes, the disaster could be forestalled.

Many thousands of cases of genetic damage need never happen. In the United Kingdom alone each year, apart from accidents at work, large numbers contract 'industrial diseases'.

At best, they will be off work for a while and may lose a considerable amount of money; but at worst they will suffer some serious disability or chronic illness and will possibly die prematurely. Obviously families and friends suffer too if a worker becomes ill or dies and even future generations will be affected if a working man or woman is exposed to a chemical causing birth defects.[34]

And this chemical exposure isn't confined to those working in factories manufacturing chemicals. We are, all of us, daily more and more at risk due to the increasing residues in food and water. Add to radioactive pollution the pollution resulting from the ever-increasing use of chemical pesticides and insecticides, lead from petrol exhausts, hydrocarbons from diesel engine fumes, and consider the 'specialist' risks we take, usually without realising it, such as

typewriter correcting fluid used by secretaries . . . the detergents, bleaches and disinfectants used by cleaners [which] can also pose a threat to health . . .[34]

and wonder at the *resilience* of man! How much longer can we continue to take that resilience for granted, though? If we sent our children onto a beach littered with broken glass and tincans, our sanity would rightly be doubted. Especially if we excused our unconcern by pointing to the well-equipped Red Cross teams who were standing by, ready to put stitches in the inevitable cuts, and transfuse blood into the badly wounded. The Red Cross would earn praise, but why was the beach in that state in the first place? And why does it take a full-scale emergency to bring us to our senses?

Perhaps this explains the fact that, out of thousands of handprints, I have no more than three or four that could truthfully be described as healthy. Several proposals have been put forward as possible solutions to the growing incidence of congenital illness – most of them technically brilliant, but in the long term as impractical and myopic as bringing in the Red Cross to cope with what should never have become an emergency at all.

One suggestion is that 'at birth skin or blood samples of every baby could be fed into a computerized genetic scanner which would note and keep a record of any chromosomal abnormalities'. Individuals applying for a marriage licence would then have to produce their cards before they were allowed to have children. But even in a completely totalitarian society there are ways to get around this, bribery being only one of them. And any advice offered to would-be parents in our own democratic system would more often than not be ignored, especially by those with a psychological investment in starting a family.

Others affirm that selective abortion is the only effective means of reducing congenital abnormalities. Although testing for damaged embryos with amniocentesis and ultrasound has proved useful in some cases, it isn't infallible, and both techniques are known to introduce an element of risk in themselves. Even using the above techniques, it hasn't been possible to state with certainty until very recently that Down's syndrome existed before the twentieth week of a woman's pregnancy.

An abortion at such a late stage can hardly fail to have the most distressing mental and physical repercussions on the mother.

Now scientists have developed another, similar test, said to be less risky. With it, identification of Down's syndrome is possible as early as the eighth to ninth week. Instead of taking a sample of amniotic fluid, a placental biopsy can be carried out and cells checked for the normal complement of chromosomes. If there are forty-seven, Down's syndrome is a certainty. If there are only forty-five, Turner's syndrome exists. Damaged chromosomes can also be identified. The new test has just been introduced in this country and, at present, is only available at King's College Hospital, London.

Mongol children are easily identified, with or without dermatoglyphic assay, but what about their parents? Mongolism is usually linked statistically with older mothers. It has been suggested that the fault occurs because the woman's ova have been exposed for longer than a younger woman's to such environmental influences as radiation (both natural and manmade), and drugs.

It will be remembered that the oocytes shed from the ovary during the reproductive years were already present before birth. Thus an egg shed by a 45-year-old woman is quite an aged cell that has been lying dormant for many years.[31]

Dermatoglyphic research suggests that there may also be an hereditary factor involved. Studies made in the fifties and sixties by Penrose, Fang and others showed 'slight but significant deviation towards the characteristic mongol type' in the parents, brothers and sisters of mongol offspring.

More than one in ten individuals has, or will develop in his or her lifetime, a disorder that has been passed down. This may be the immediate result of dominant maternal/paternal genes or it may come about if one individual affected by a chemical or other mutagen mates and passes on a defective recessive gene. Or the damage may be caused by pathological changes at the molecular level which may or may not involve genetic material. Cell membranes or enzymes may be harmed, and metabolic processes disrupted leaving DNA, the conductor of the enzyme 'band', unable to communicate his requirements to the musicians, or RNA.

A great many chemical substances, ionizing and other forms of radiation such as ultra-violet, together with a variety of viruses and pathogenic bacteria are all agents of biological damage in man. The damaging effects are essentially twofold:

1 Somatic effects occurring in body tissue exposed to the agent and acting directly on the health of the individual.
2 Genetic (or hereditary) effects occurring in the gonads (the germ cells) and affecting the health of descendants through several generations . . .

The genetic effects of exposure to pollutants, mutagenesis, are . . . limited to the germ cells of the body. The primitive germ cells of an individual are formed at an early prenatal stage of cell differentiation, and damage to the hereditary material can occur at any stage of an individual's reproductive life.[28]

Damage to genetic material *in utero* is reflected in palmar and plantar dermatoglyphs being distorted from the norm in significant ways. Pollutants can affect germ cells – sperm and ova, so that the results of exposure are only seen in the offspring of those contaminated – *and* somatic, or general body cells, simultaneously. In up to 60 per cent of the total number of miscarriages the foetus or embryo is found to have chromosomal abnormalities of one kind or another.

There are several kinds of structural abnormality. A chromosome may snap in two and part of it disappear. This is referred to as an *unbalanced translocation* and is likely to lead to serious birth defects. When pieces break off two or more chromosomes and then change places, a *balanced translocation* is said to have occurred and serious defects are less likely. When a single chromosome breaks in two places and these reverse position and rejoin, *inversion* has occurred. This may or may not have serious consequences, depending on the particular chromosomes involved, and may be an hereditary fault.

One chromosome sticking to another during cell division is called *nondisjunction*, and disorders characterized by an extra chromosome are known as *trisomic*. Down's syndrome is usually but not invariably due to trisomy of autosome 21. The twenty-two pairs of autosomes are numbered according to size, starting with the largest. Number 21 is one of the smallest. When one of a pair of chromosomes is missing, the abnormality is called *monosomic*.

Various striking anomalies in the arrangement of dermal ridges on palms and soles are associated with chromosomal aberrations. Abnormalities may be divided into two main types, according to whether the autosomes or the sex chromosomes are involved.[27]

Problems with the sex chromosomes are more common than with the autosomes, and lead to sterility, impotence, menstrual problems, and sexual ambiguity. These, too, are indicated in the hands.

If only some organs or tissues are affected (some cells being normal, and others having the extra chromosome), the resulting condition is described as *chromosomal mosaicism.* In Down's syndrome, for example, if trisomy of chromosome 21 exists in all, or almost all, the cells mongoloid features will be unmistakable. The features are well-known and include gross retardation of growth, mental defectiveness, small mouth and small, slanted eyes. Heart defects and malformation of intestines and digestive equipment mean that mongols rarely survive early adulthood. However, if 40 per cent or more of the cells are normal, with up to 60 per cent having an extra chromosome, the victim is a *mosaic mongol.* In this case,

the features of mongolism will be present but are likely to be milder, depending upon which organs have normal cells.[19]

According to Professor Penrose and his associates, the studies they conducted on the dermatoglyphs of mosaic mongols indicated that,

the degree of distortion is not closely related to the proportion of abnormal cells, as demonstrated in cultures, nor to the level of mental development attained.

The hands of mongoloid types are characteristically chunky; broad, short, and deep at the palm with thick, stubby fingers.

A transverse palmar crease, the so-called 'simian line' is often present, while occasionally the distal flexion crease on the fifth finger is absent. On the feet there is usually a deep crease between the second and third toes.[27]

The dermatoglyphs themselves are distinctive and were first noted by Cummins and Midlo in 1936. Patterns on the hypothenar eminence (the fleshy pad at the base of the hand and under the little finger) are found in 85 per cent of mongols, compared with 12 per cent in non-mongols. The ridges themselves are often malformed in characteristic ways, and though there are minor racial variations, Down's syndrome is recognized by common features the world over.

Galton pioneered the way, and Cummins and Midlo consolidated it so that others could follow. Now it seems there's a fork in the road ahead – dermatoglyphic experts are breaking new ground in the fields of genetic counselling and prenatal diagnosis.

There is now the medical technology to prevent birth defects through pre-natal diagnosis, to detect the carriers of genetic disease though they have no obvious symptoms, to diagnose certain genetic disorders at birth, and to provide some specific treatments.[19]

It's only natural that would-be parents should wonder if their children are going to be normal, especially when the mass media tends to spotlight – and exaggerate in the minds of the public – the numbers and plight of the handicapped and disabled. It's easy to lose sight of the fact that, of every hundred babies born, an average of ninety-seven are free from major birth defects. A statistic, of course, that is hardly reassuring to a pregnant mum, and these two or three abnormal births are cause for concern. Fear inhibits many couples with no history of inherited disease, and stops them trying for a baby.

Unfortunately, genetic counselling facilities in the United Kingdom are limited and/or expensive. It is only offered by the National Health Service to prospective parents with special reason to believe there's a risk of conceiving abnormal embryos. One of the few centres offering such guidance is the Kennedy-Galton Centre for Clinical Genetics at Harperbury Hospital, Hertfordshire. The Centre was set up twenty years ago by Professor Penrose on his retirement in 1965 from the Galton Chair of Eugenics. With Professor Penrose in charge it was inevitable that dermatoglyphic analysis would have a part to play in any investigation.

The borders of more and more scientific disciplines are starting to overlap: to become less well-defined. One of these is socio-biology, a rather controversial newcomer which holds that our social behaviour is not so much learned as genetically regulated. Altruism becomes 'genetic selfishness' in the jargon of socio-biology.

The same general principle is behind the theory of bio-types, itself an extension of the ancient doctrine relating personality and health to the four humours. The idea is that we are biologically susceptible to certain diseases because we have inherited, not only obvious physical weaknesses from our parents, but also patterns of behaviour. The fact that mood changes are chemically related is well known. They are recognized symptoms in many degenerative illnesses, and acknowledged side effects of some drug treatments.

The common theme linking dermatoglyphics with these other disciplines seems to be the belief that to a greater or lesser degree we inherit much of our potential – whether positive or negative – from our forebears. This is where the promise of dermatoglyphic analysis lies. As a potent tool in the hands of genetic counsellors, it should be available not only to those who are known to be at risk by reason of their age or a history of disorders in the family, but to anyone wishing for reassurance.

At present there is wide agreement that the heredity of most dermatoglyphic features conforms to a polygenic system, with individual genes contributing a small additive effect. Modern cytogenetic methods, which allow rather precise identification of chromosomes, are certain to be of great value in studying the correlations between individual chromosome aberrations and dermatoglyphic features and may lead to establishing the loci of genes that influence dermatoglyphics.[21]

Improved techniques for identifying and correlating ridge patterns with specific genetic disorders must lead – sooner or later – to a more widespread understanding and acceptance of dermatoglyphic potential. There is no reason why any general practitioner should not be able to assess and interpret standard ridge abnormalities, given a short but comprehensive grounding in the necessary techniques. In Germany, the science is already a vital diagnostic tool for thousands of doctors. A training programme in dermatoglyphic analysis is available at all major German universities and is routine procedure in Germany and other parts of Europe, according to Dr Alexander Rodewald, who designed the programme. Dr Rodewald claims to predict, with 80 per cent accuracy, the chances of a new-born baby developing heart disease, cancer, leukaemia, mental illness – and even criminal tendencies – by checking the baby's hand and foot prints.

American experts researching the same field are convinced that the future of dermatoglyphics is not limited to mere diagnosis – as accurate as that can be. Having determined which people are potentially at risk of developing, say, cancer, diabetes, or schizoid tendencies in their lifetime, the next step is, quite obviously, to stop it happening; to instigate preventative measures. There is no doubt that tremendous advances have been made, particularly since the invention of the electron microscope, but I'm sure we still have a long way to go before the hand yields all its secrets.

Let's take a look at what has already been accomplished by dermatoglyphicists and researchers in practical terms . . . and a peek at the future of palmistry in the twenty-first century.

Part Two

Palmistry in Practice

7

Handprinting – Methods and Equipment

Dermatoglyphics offer at least two major advantages as an aid to the diagnosis of medical disorders: (1) the epidermal ridge patterns on the hands and soles are fully developed at birth and, thereafter, remain unchanged for life; (2) scanning of the ridge patterns or recording their permanent impressions (i.e., prints) can be accomplished rapidly, inexpensively, and without trauma to the patient.

A number of methods for recording dermatoglyphics exists. The methods vary in their requirements for equipment, time, and experience and in the quality of the prints produced.

Blanka Schaumann and Milton Alter,
Dermatoglyphics in Medical Disorders[21]

Handprinting is an essential part of scientific hand reading whether you're a dermatoglyphic researcher, a biologist, or a palmist. Try looking at your own palms and you'll see what I mean. The lines, or creases, may be clear enough (this varies tremendously from person to person), but the ridge patterns are almost invisible to the naked eye, even under a magnifying glass.

A scientific study needs permanent records that can be compared, contrasted, and otherwise analysed. Handprinting is really an art in its own right, and one that is still being developed. No one has yet come up with a consistently accurate, foolproof method of committing those all-important patterns to paper. Of all the methods practised, the police identification system seems to come closest, but the equipment required is elaborate and cumbersome, not exactly what you'd describe as portable. And there are occasions when portable equipment is invaluable.

At this stage, it would be useful to investigate some of the many hand- (and foot-) printing methods in use today. It is recommended that you do make an attempt to take your own prints. It will certainly give you an insight into the sort of problems that can occur and, as you go on to read the practical, as opposed to theoretical, part of this book, add another dimension to it – personal involvement.

Whoever you are, if you're taking prints, the requirements are the same. You'll want good, clear, undistorted prints with no smudges or smears, and plenty of patience, because whichever the method adopted, only practice can make perfect prints. The need for permanent, easily filed records has led to many variations on this basic theme. Weird and wonderful devices abound. I've seen and heard tell of some very clumsy and awkward to use gadgets and gismos, many of which appeared to have come straight off Heath Robinson's drawing board.

Taking the actual *finger* prints presents few problems. Getting an accurate representation of palms and soles isn't quite so easy. In effect we're translating a three-dimensional image into one and some of the contours – lumps, bumps, and assorted convexities and concavities – can be quite a nightmare, especially for the novice. Photocopiers have been suggested as a solution but give no more than a very crude and distorted picture. Useless for serious studies. The most promising solution is, of course, the ubiquitous computer. With a sufficiently sophisticated graphics system, I'm sure this is where the answer lies.

New Scotland Yard already has a Videofile information system capable of storing, comparing and retrieving up to three million or so separate fingerprint images. Technological advances have now made it possible for the computer to recognize individual finger- and hand-prints, and compare them with a list of authorized personnel. Increasing use of such techniques is envisaged in banks and other high security establishments. If a computer can be 'taught' to do this, it can also be programmed to print out a picture of the hand, complete with skin-ridge and sweat-pore detail.

At present there is no doubt that such techniques would be prohibitively expensive for the majority of dermatoglyphic researchers, who will continue to use the older and time-honoured methods we're about to describe. With one or two exceptions, all of these require ink, paper, a roller, and an inking slab. These are the bare essentials. If the printing medium is oil-based, a solvent and/or a proprietary brand of cleanser such as Swarfega will be needed, together with plenty of sturdy cloths or tissues. A water-based product (as used by the authors) has a major advantage here. It washes off quickly and easily with a minimum of warm, soapy water – essential when printing babies and children.

POLICE FINGER-PRINTING

Although, strictly speaking, police fingerprinting methods seem out-of-place in a book of this nature, we're going to describe them because they're a lot more efficient in practice than many others and could easily be adapted for use by scientists in different fields. In police work, the subject isn't always cooperative. Far from it, if he happens to be a criminal or suspected criminal; so the technique must be simple and straightforward, and able to be applied at short notice by officers with little or no formal training.

Equipment
1 A glass or metal plate, approximately 12 in by 4 in. This is sometimes but not always mounted on a sturdy wooden frame.
2 A photographic-type 'squeegee' roller, for distributing the ink evenly along the surface of the plate.
3 Oil-based fingerprinting ink in collapsible tubes.
4 Specially designed forms with spaces for the individual digits and thumbs, a palm print, and a 'rolled' palm print. One of these is used for the left and one for the right hand.
5 A device for holding the form in position so that it doesn't slip in operation.
6 Lead-free petrol, spirit, or other chemical medium for harmlessly cleaning hands and equipment after use.
7 A medium-sized magnifying glass for examining detail.
8 Plenty of cloths for cleaning up.
9 A portable stand, or small table, designed specially for the work.

Additional equipment for palmprinting alone supplements the above. A convex wooden block, approximately 12 in by 9 in by 2 in at its deepest point is used in combination with a convex metal plate of similar dimensions. The former is the printing block and it's covered with a thin sheet of corrugated rubber, smooth side uppermost to give resilience and counter problems caused by uneven palmar contours. The metal plate takes the ink.

Printing
Fingers (or palms) are first cleaned with spirit. If all perspiration or dampness isn't removed smudgy prints result. Hard, dry skin may need soaking in warm water first. Best results are obtained if the hands are wiped, but not dried thoroughly.

A few drops of ink are rolled onto the plate with the roller until the correct consistency is achieved. Experience is the best guide here, but the film of ink should look matt rather than wet and shiny, and the resulting prints should be clear and sharp, the ridges black, furrows white, without blur. Room temperature may affect the consistency of the ink. In cold weather it may be necessary to warm the plate slightly.

In police work, the most important part of the finger is the tip and this is rolled onto the form to ensure that the complete ridge pattern is recorded. Classification is impossible unless it is rolled correctly as the system relies on the officer being able to count the ridges between 'core' and 'delta'. See Figure 34 for an illustration of the problem.

Each digit in turn is placed on the inked plate sideways on, the extreme edge of the nail touching the plate, and with the subject's palm facing the operator. The finger tip is then rolled lightly *towards* the operator whose own index finger is placed lightly on top of the subject's to ensure even pressure throughout. Exactly the same procedure is repeated as each print is committed to paper. The pad is then re-inked and a separate

Figure 34   Problems of classification created by the insufficient rolling of the fingers.
A shows the delta of the twinned loop missing through insufficient rolling of the finger.
B shows the print of the same finger properly rolled and disclosing the delta missing from A.
In the case of print A it should be noted that insufficient rolling has prevented not only the disclosure of the right-hand delta but has failed to reveal the correct pattern. Superficially A appears to be a print of the loop type

A   B

impression made of the four fingers together, without rolling them, after which the thumbs are printed separately.

Next, a sheet of paper is clipped into place over the rubber-faced wooden block described earlier and the hand is inked, from base to finger tips, and the print transferred to the appropriate section of the preprinted form. In each instance – inking and printing – the base of the hand contacts the medium – ink or paper – first. The operator gradually and gently applies pressure with his own hand, again from base to finger tips, to reduce the possibility of smudging and distortion to a minimum.

For police purposes, a second palm print of each hand is required, this time including the skin-ridge patterns from the extreme outer edge of the hand. The technique for this is an adaptation of the previously described 'rolling' method.

On those occasions when there is an objection to the hands being inked – a householder who's been robbed, or bank staff, for instance – specially treated paper is often used instead. Fingers and palm are impressed on a pad impregnated with a harmless developing agent and placed on the paper. The print then starts to appear, getting darker by the minute as a chemical reaction occurs. Too much fluid, though, and the ridge differentiation is lost.

Another method involves applying a thin film of glycerine to the ridged skin with cotton wool, pressing the hand onto a piece of smooth white paper, and applying graphite powder to the sheet until the ridges show up. Surplus powder is removed by tapping, and the print sealed with transparent adhesive tape. The main problem here is judging the correct amount of glycerine.

DERMATOGLYPHIC FINGERPRINTING

The dermatoglyphic expert, like the police officer, requires permanent impressions of prints for his records but, unlike the policeman, the scientific researcher is scanning his prints for similarities, rather than differences. The same degree of clarity is, however, required by both parties.

Equipment
1 A glass or metal inking slab, large enough to take a large hand, or a large foot.
2 A roller for distributing the ink on the slab.

3   A supply of printer's ink.
4   A supply of good quality, non-absorbent paper, preferably with a slightly glazed surface.
5   A sponge-rubber pressure-pad.

Printing
Sweat, oil, and dirt should be removed from the skin first with a lavish application of soap and water. The experts follow this with ethyl alcohol and ether to make absolutely sure the skin to be printed is suitably primed. A little ink is placed on the inking slab and spread, thinly and evenly, with the roller. The hand – or palm, or finger – is pressed against the inked surface and the inked area pressed onto a sheet of the glazed paper.

This method is said to give good results with adults and 'cooperative children', though prints of 'palms and soles obtained in this manner are often imperfect'. Scientists certainly don't seem to be the most practical of people! A simple way round the problem is to follow police initiative and place a sponge-rubber pressure-pad under the paper when an imprint of palm or sole is required. Some operators get results by rolling the palm over a paper-covered jar or bottle. I can't imagine this would work for plantar surfaces, though, so it's hardly surprising to find that 'technical difficulties' are blamed for the comparative scarcity of sole and toe prints. It is certainly far easier to roll fingers than toes, and the ridged skin of both palms and soles can extend well beyond their bases (see Figure 35).

There are several adaptations of this basic idea. One of these recommends the use of the rubber pad during both inking and printing. The area to be printed is placed on a previously inked, paraffined paper lying atop the rubber pad. The ridged skin is then applied to a clean sheet of paper placed on the pad.

Another modification entails the use of a roller with a rigid centre and a foam rubber sleeve (similar to a paint roller). A sheet of glossy paper is fixed, shiny surface facing outwards, round the roller whose diameter would be not less than 3 inches. The hand is inked, and the print then taken by 'moving the roller from the wrist crease toward the fingertips in one smooth sweep'. I haven't tried this myself, but I'd imagine quite a lot could go wrong.

In America, commercial ink printing sets are available from Hollister Inc., 211E Chicago Avenue, Chicago, Illinois, 60611, USA. These are specially suited to obstetric units where prints are used to identify

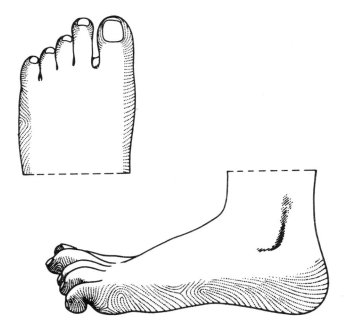

Figure 35   Normal plantar ridging can extend quite a way up the foot

new-born infants. Some users find that the quality of the prints leaves much to be desired while other experienced field workers recommend them highly. Once again, good results are more likely with practice.

One particularly ingenious method uses Indian ink, transparent sticky tape, and paper. Indian ink is painted onto the palm and finger tips (or sole and toes). When the ink is completely dry, strips of adhesive tape are rolled onto the skin surface from one side to the other till the whole of the ridged area is covered. The tape is then removed, strip by strip, and transferred to the sheet of paper. With this method there is, apparently, no problem printing the awkward contours of palm and sole. The remaining ink is easily removed with soap and water.

Adhesive tape can also be used with dry pigments such as chalk, or powdered graphite applied to clean, dry skin surfaces. The clear adhesive film sold for covering books, etc., is ideal for this. Oil pastel crayon, and stick graphite, are other alternatives. These techniques can be readily adapted to all types of subject, including young babies (even newborn) and individuals with misshapen and malformed hands and feet. Be sure to mark left and right hands accurately.

A more sophisticated technique involves spraying or painting a chemical solution – polyvinyl formal in ethylene dichloride – onto the skin. In ten to fifteen seconds, a thin film forms. This is removed with transparent vinyl sticky tape in the same way as before. The tape, complete with film, is mounted on a slide and examined under a microscope. The main disadvantage here is the risk of allergic reaction and a skin test should always be done first. I have seen the hands of some research workers virtually destroyed by the formaldehyde and other chemicals they insist are essential for the production of good prints. One in particular comes to mind. His own skin-ridge patterns were illegible, and nails and finger tips split and permanently fissured.

Photographic techniques have so far proved too expensive and/or inadequate for reproducing accurate images of the whole hand. Apparatus specially designed for fingerprinting infants and newborns has had limited success in the United States. Though the prints obtained are clear, only areas in direct contact with the rigid surface of a prism can be photographed, considerably reducing the value of this apparatus for general dermatoglyphic analysis.

Hygrophotographic film has been successfully used, but the process is time consuming – and therefore expensive. For this reason, it is rarely used, except for special studies. The film reacts with perspiration on the surface of the skin and, developed as a negative, clearly shows the skin ridges, pores, and active sweat glands. The hygrophotographic film must first be exposed to the light and allowed to darken after which the subject's hand or foot is placed on it for a variable period of time – a few seconds, or minutes, depending on his rate of perspiration.

Another photographic method involves moistening a thick sheet of blotting paper with a developing solution. The hand or foot is pressed against this for a few seconds, and then placed on a sheet of photographic paper. The prints are then developed in the normal way. In yet another, lanolin is applied to the skin to be printed, the skin surface applied to the photographic film or plate, and the film or plate processed in the usual way.

Radiodermatography – that is, the use of x-rays in dermatoglyphic analysis – was attempted as early as 1918.

Beclere massaged bismuth carbonate, a radiopaque contrast material, into the skin surface after first treating the skin with lanolin. X-rays taken afterwards revealed not only bone structures but also dermatoglyphic patterns.[21]

Other mediums, many later found to be toxic, were also tried, including barium, lead salts, commercial white oil paint, and zinc bromide solutions. Tantalum powder is applied before x-raying the hand today. In general, the same objections apply as before. The process is complicated, expensive and time consuming but it is useful when correlating the position of ridges and lines with underlying bony structures, or in criminal dactyloscopy when it is impossible to check the fingerprints by any other method.

Printing malformed hands and feet, and the ridge patterns of non-human primates presents exceptional difficulties. One way of overcoming this is to make a plastic or dental wax impression. Latex rubber is another possibility. The impression is treated as a mould from which plaster casts may be made. Until computer science and photographic techniques become sufficiently sophisticated to cope with 'awkward' hands that are bent, twisted, or constantly on the move, a variation on the mould theme is the only option available.

SCIENTIFIC HAND ANALYSIS

Scientific hand analysis has its own handprinting requirements. The hand analyst studies the shape of the hand – which means he prefers to have his prints accurately outlined – as well as the lines and skin ridges. For character analysis, it isn't necessary to roll the fingers – a direct print is enough – but the thumb is printed and outlined separately: it is an important reference point for the scientific palmist (see Brandon-Jones, *Practical Palmistry*, Rider).

Early in my career as a hand analyst, I developed my own handprinting regime. Having already come up against all the problems that *could* occur using the techniques available at the time, I decided enough was enough. It can be quite embarrassing having to take a client's prints two, or even three times, because you haven't been able to get the all-important bit at the centre of the palms. It was happening to me far too often!

Necessity is indeed the mother of invention. After a week or so spent studying the problem from all angles (I have the type of hand known as the 'Analytical'), I designed and built my own handprinting platform. With minor modifications, I am still using it today, and most of my

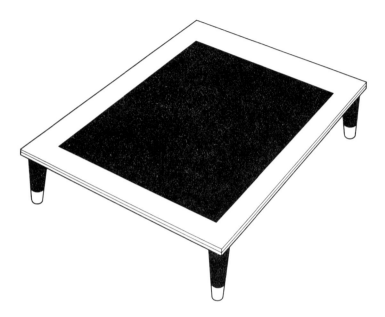

Figure 36   This table or platform is easily made. Plywood will do. Cut two pieces 14 in square from $\frac{1}{4}$ in ply. From one cut out a square of 11 × 11 in leaving a $1\frac{1}{2}$ in frame. From the other 14 in square cut out a 9 in square to leave a $2\frac{1}{2}$ in frame. Glue the two frames firmly together with wood glue. Place a piece of 3/16 in rubber sheeting 11 × 11 in square over the hole and fix securely with good quality adhesive. Add legs from any DIY store and after a coat or two of clear varnish your handprinting table is ready for use

successful students possess a similar piece of equipment. An added advantage is that it is easily transportable (see Figure 36).

Equipment
1   Handprinting platform, as described. Or, and this is definitely a second-best alternative to the platform (but better than most of the dermatoglyphic techniques described), a firm, yet flexible, latex rubber pad of the sort used by typists under their machines. It must be resistant enough to enable the operator to outline the print without his pen going through the paper.
2   A glass or square of laminate such as Formica, or any nonporous,

easy-to-clean, rigid surface on which to spread the ink. This should be about ten inches square.

3 A four-inch rubber roller as used in photographic or art work. This should be filed down at both ends before use on the palms. As we've seen, problems often arise in inking and printing the hands because of the undulations and curves thereon. Figure 38 shows the roller after modification.

4 Rowney's block printing ink. Their water-based lino printing ink was ideal for handprinting – but obviously not for lino printing as it has been discontinued. The block printing ink is the next best thing, though it tends to be rather sloppy. Black is most suitable, particularly if a photocopy is required.

5 A supply of good quality, A4-sized paper, nonporous. Some paper sold for photocopying has the right degree of glossiness.

6 The inside, or skeleton, of a ballpoint pen to use when outlining the prints. The reason for this soon becomes apparent if you take the trouble to outline your own hand twice – once with the insert, and once with the complete pen. The difference between the two can be quite remarkable. The outline made with the insert is a far more accurate representation of the actual size of your hand.

Figure 37 Roller, as stocked by good art shops and photographic suppliers

Figure 38 Same roller, with ends filed and adapted for printing

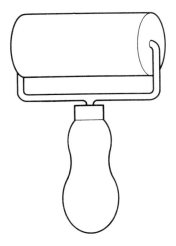

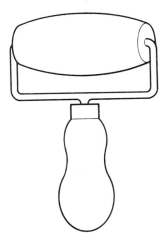

Printing

Squeeze out a little ink onto the sheet of glass or laminate, and spread it with the roller until the *roller* is coated thinly and evenly throughout its length. The ink tends to accumulate at the ends of the roller. This should be removed with a tissue before the roller is applied to the hand.

Make sure the hand is relaxed, then, starting from the wrist, roll the ink onto the palm, fingers and thumb. Use the filed-off ends of the roller to get into the awkward centre of the palm. When the whole palm is evenly covered in ink the subject places it, base first, on the sheet of paper you've positioned in the centre of the sheet of rubber.

Try to ensure that the hand doesn't twitch or move. If it does, you'll find that the prints are smudged. With practice even printing the hands of children or the mentally retarded can be done efficiently and accurately, so don't despair. Once the hand is in place, steady it with your free hand while using the other to press upwards from underneath. The handprinting table enables you in this way to pay particular attention to the centre of the subject's palm.

If the mounts surrounding this area are deep, or the palm is hollow, or the fingers are stiff and inflexible as in arthritis, the latex rubber pad alone will be virtually useless. If you continue to take prints with large white spaces where the palmar markings should be, and you don't have the special table, place a small wodge of soft tissue under the sheet of paper and try again. There should be some improvement. When the mounts are really deep and firm though, there's no alternative to the table if you're determined to get first class prints.

Now mark round the print with the innards of your ballpoint. To the hand analyst, this outline alone can provide enough 'meat' about the subject's character to fill six or seven pages of typescript. Without an outline, the print is quite different. The thumb is printed and outlined separately on the same sheet. Rolled finger tip prints, showing the full extent of the ridging, can be added to the same sheet, along its length.

When you've taken the prints of several different people you'll find that, not only are their hands unique, each set of prints will vary in quality from the next. This isn't necessarily due to the operator's negligence. Some hands are drier than others and absorb more ink, so the print itself will be darker. If the hand is moist, there will be insufficient definition between the ridges, or smudging, especially of the finger tip patterns. Some hands don't seem to want to reveal their secrets at all, and for no apparent reason every print is faint and the ridges almost impossible to identify, even with a magnifying glass. It's important though not to overlook the obvious – the solution may be quite simple. Hand or barrier cream should always be washed away thoroughly before printing the hands. Should the print seem hazy or watery, add a little more ink and roll well before making a second attempt. If the ridging is thick and black, and the print smeary have the subject wash and dry his hands well – soap and water is enough – and try again having added a *drop* or two of water, and rolling it until the correct consistency has been achieved.

Having obtained your prints and cleaned up your subject you'll need to record a certain amount of additional information. Whatever your speciality, this will normally include his name, age and date of birth, and the date the prints were taken. A police identification bureau official will proceed to analyse the prints, and record his conclusions as per the formula laid down by Sir Edward Henry in 1901. Though there have since been numerous developments in this specialist field and the actual procedure streamlined enormously, the basic technique hasn't changed much.

The dermatoglyphicist requires additional information about his subjects' parents, and their parents before them. He may even have taken the handprints of several generations, together with details of their racial group, health patterns and individual constitution. These are then carefully cross-indexed and filed or fed into a computer along with other relevant data.

The scientific hand analyst, for his part, normally fills out a comprehensive data sheet, especially if he is to provide a typed report of his analysis, or a cassette. He needs to know whether his client is left-handed or right – or perhaps ambidextrous. It's important for his purposes to know if the skin is soft, fine, or leathery, if the back of the hand is finely covered or thickly matted with hair, and whether the hands are normally hot, cool, or cold. The colour of hands and palms, the colour, shape, and state of the fingernails, and the degree of padding on the palms are all important clues to character and vitality for the scientific palmist. By means of the supplementary data sheet, he is effectively able to reinstate the two dimensions lost when he took the client's prints.

Jaquin, the chirologist, was convinced that the finger pad patterns alone possessed vital psychological significance. He goes further, linking psychological and emotional make-up with physical weaknesses when he states that 'parallel with certain mental or emotional states there exist certain chemical conditions of the body created by these conditions of the

	Loop pattern Adaptability. Mental flexibility.	Whorl pattern Persistent. Individualizes sense of taste.	Arch pattern Undemonstrative. Practical. Reliable.	Composite (Intertwined loops) Duality of mind. Indecisive.	Tented Arch Extreme sensitivity.
Thumb	Can adapt manner of approach to suit varying circumstances.	Independent and original. May be secretive, but as a means of self-protection. Stubborn, Dogmatic.	Quick and efficient. Decision maker. Practical rather than abstract thinkers who like to get things done, to feel worthy.	Indecisive when important decisions needed. But able to see both sides of question or problem.	*Extremely Rare* Sensitive to the point of being prickly. Rigidly fixed outlook.
Index	Problem solver, by hook or by crook – never thrown completely by unexpected.	The specialist, innovator and non-conformist. Needs a niche or vocation.	Good, capable, trustworthy managers on whom others instinctively rely. May repress own needs to benefit others. Often feels 'used'.	Useful for lawyers, police, administrators, judges.	Very sensitive hearing. Tends to espouse 'causes' energetically and fixedly.
2nd finger	Open-minded. Not bound by any one doctrine, religion, or belief. Adaptable.	May belong to weird or outlandish sects. Abides by the law till it stands in the way, then ignores it.	Religiously drawn to simple faiths such as Quaker, Salvation Army, Methodist, rather than High Church pomp and ceremony.	*Rare* Conflicting spiritual and material values, leading to guilt and much soul searching.	*Very Rare* Home and traditional values are almost sacred. Idealistic.
Ring finger	Good team worker. Enjoys stimulation of new ideas and concepts, re daily life and the Arts. Artistic.	Original taste in food, clothes and decor. Does not follow fashion.	*Extremely rare* unless part of a complete set. Artistic and emotional expression tends towards the practical. Often a loner.	*Sometimes found* Tends to hold independent views. Slow to make decisions. Followers of fads and fancies.	*Rare* Highly strung. Highly developed artistic awareness. May be musically gifted.
Little finger	Emotionally responsive. Versatile. Able to express feelings.	Individual way of expressing self. Fixed opinions. Difficulty communicating ideas.	*Extremely rare* Can't small talk. Reticent and artistic. Emotional expression	Diplomatic. Dislikes ruffling feathers or atmospheres. Conciliatory.	*Extremely rare* Fixed ideas. Lacks spontaneity. Suspicious of others.

psyche which predispose to definite types of pathological processes.' A preponderance of any one type of pattern might therefore be expected to predispose its owner to a particular type of ailment, and this does seem to be the case. The chart on p. 120 correlates pattern types, personality types, and emotional attitudes. I'm sure you'll find it an interesting exercise to compare your own, and any other prints you may take, with those listed on the chart. Bear in mind, of course, that these are just the five basic patterns and don't take into account more complex, composite arrangements that you'll meet from time to time.

The way you take your prints will be a matter of personal preference. My students have no trouble with the 'approved' method I describe here which seems to give the most consistent results. Armed with your prints, you'll be in a far better position to understand the dermatoglyphicist's work.

8

Dermatoglyphic Nomenclature

Our ignorance of ourselves is of a peculiar nature. It does not arise from difficulty in procuring the necessary information, from its inaccuracy, or from its scarcity. On the contrary, it is due to the extreme abundance and confusion of the data accumulated about itself by humanity during the course of the ages; also to the division of man into an almost infinite number of fragments by the sciences that have endeavoured to study his body and his consciousness. This knowledge, to a large extent, has not been utilized. In fact, it is barely utilizable. Its sterility manifests itself in the meagreness of the classical abstractions, of the schemata that are the basis of medicine, hygiene, education, sociology, and political economy. There is, however, a living and rich reality buried in the enormous mass of definitions, observations, doctrines, desires, and dreams representing man's efforts towards a knowledge of himself . . .

Alexis Carrel, *Man the Unknown*[1]

Until now, the main thrust of dermatoglyphic research has been directed into the area of genetics rather than general or preventative medicine. This potentially potent tool has been limited to the diagnosis of chromosomal defects, its use not considered as a practical means of identifying latent disorders, nor as an aid to short-circuiting or reversing the process of disease. Yet the 'unorthodox' workers – the hand analysts and psycho-chirologists – have reason to believe that the human hand invariably provides clues to impending mental and physical illness, not necessarily triggered genetically, and long before conventionally acceptable symptoms start to show.

The lines and the skin ridges seem to respond immediately to prolonged stress, external or internal, whatever the cause. As a hand analyst, I feel that this is the time to make a health check, to make an assessment of the individual's biochemical efficiency at cell level (where disease invariably starts), his nervous system, and rate of enzyme production. This is an area of dermatoglyphics which has been sadly neglected, investigation might provide valuable time during which the foundations of health could be strengthened *before* major structural damage occurs.

The skin-ridge patterns themselves don't change appreciably during life, though in some conditions they may deteriorate to the point where pattern identification is impossible. Obviously, as a child grows to adulthood they will expand, just as in old age they may shrink slightly, but the actual number of ridges and their relative position on our palms and soles is as fixed and permanent as the inheritance they represent.

Recording and checking the condition of an earlier with a later set of handprints is a relatively straightforward process, even with a simple magnifying glass. A record of the dermatoglyphs can be made quickly and painlessly and, unlike x-rays and other investigatory techniques, there are no known side-effects – unless getting your hands dirty is a phobia!

As our hands are changing all the time – lines come and go, become finer or thicker, ridges atrophy and recover – taking and comparing check prints in order to assess the effect of medical treatment on our ailments is a real possibility in the near future.

Advances in computer technology signal a quantum leap forward for dermatoglyphic research and hand analysis. When specialized cameras and electron microscopes become more generally available and we can magnify the dermatoglyphs to a high degree, without distortion, the 'new' science of dermatoglyphics will come into its own. These innovations could provide the science with the most significant impetus it has received since the invention of the microscope over four hundred years ago.

The last advance of any note occurred when the relationship between chromosomal abnormalities and unusual skin-ridge markings was first established. Scientific interest reached a peak. So many and diverse were the disciplines studying this intriguing subject, including biologists, anthropologists, and geneticists (all generating their own jargon in an effort to comprehend ideas and concepts they'd never before encountered) that an international symposium was set up to sort out their semantic problems.

Professor Penrose convened the meeting which took place in September 1967. He was no longer at the Galton Laboratory but was nevertheless extremely active in the field and felt that the time was ripe for standardizing the terminology used in research work and papers. The resulting *Memorandum on Dermatoglyphic Nomenclature* was published in 1968 and adopted without too much dissent. The symposium attracted fifteen participants from seven different countries, and was quite an historic occasion in yet another respect. It was officially recognized for the first time that the palmar and plantar creases were anatomically related to the dermal ridges, and that, as such, they have 'useful clinical applications'.

We've already noted the names given by field workers to the lines of the hand. Perhaps a crash course in dermatoglyphic terminology wouldn't go amiss here before we go on to examine the detailed work being carried out by dermatoglyphic researchers.

Dermatoglyphicists are working with anatomical structure in miniature. For detailed analysis of the palmar patterns and to facilitate subsequent discussion of their findings, the development of a new language – or jargon – was inevitable. Equally inevitable is the fact that, if we're to understand what the experts are trying to do, we have to know what they're talking about. Some of the basic terms are self-explanatory, and some we've already encountered in the text.

THE ANATOMY OF PALMAR AND PLANTAR RIDGES
(see Figure 39)

Epidermal ridges cover the palmar surface of hands and fingers, and the plantar surface of feet and toes. Some New World monkeys also exhibit ridging of the skin on that part of their tails used to suspend their bodies as they move through the jungle, facilitating a secure grip both for locomotion and grasping.

Epidermal furrows are the depressions between the skin ridges.

The *sweat gland duct pores* lie along the centres of the skin ridges and help to keep the skin moist and supple – another aid to gripping and grasping. Dampness also improves the sense of touch. It has recently been discovered that not only the papillary ridges, but the size, shape, number and distribution of the pores is unique to the individual.

The *stratum corneum* is the uppermost layer of the epidermis, the layer of dead, cornified cells we see with the naked eye. Under this is the *stratum germinativum* where the growing cells, destined to replace the outer layer

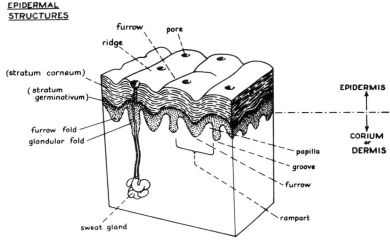

EPIDERMAL STRUCTURES

furrow
ridge
pore
(stratum corneum)
(stratum germinativum)
EPIDERMIS
furrow fold
glandular fold
CORIUM or DERMIS
papilla
groove
furrow
sweat gland
rampart
STRUCTURES OF CORIUM

Figure 39   The anatomy of palmar and plantar ridges

as it wears away, germinate. This consists of *furrow folds* which follow the contours of the superficial folds in health (some illnesses are characterized by dermal and epidermal atrophy resulting in flattening of the ridges), and *glandular folds*.

Beneath the stratum germinativum is the *corium* or *dermis*. In this layer are to be found the blood vessels and glands. The formations here are designated *grooves, furrows, papillae*, and *ramparts*.

ASSESSING PAPILLARY RIDGE DIMENSION

In order to make accurate comparisons between the ridged skin of different individuals, terms of reference must obviously be standardized. Since the true dimensions of a ridge can vary from those shown in a print, depending on the degree of pressure applied during printing, one hundred per cent accuracy in reproducing the skin-ridge patterns in this way is impossible. Despite these limitations, however, much of value has been achieved by those interested in this aspect of the ridges.

Ridge breadth is defined by measuring the distance between the centre of one epidermal furrow and the centre of the next, along a line at right angles to the direction of the furrows. The *printed width* will, as we've seen, vary according to the pressure applied by the person taking the prints. When making a comparative study, therefore, it would be best if all the prints were to be made by the same person. Mean breadth is normally estimated by counting the number of ridges on a line one centimetre long, crossing them at right angles. The distribution of total finger-ridge counts in normal subjects and subjects suffering various chromosomal abnormalities have been found to differ significantly. Variation in ridge density in different areas of the same hand is quite common.

RIDGE STRUCTURE IN DETAIL

The structure of each and every ridge distinguishes it from its neighbour. All have their individual peculiarities, designated *minutiae* by Francis Galton and still identified as such today (see Figure 40). There are eight basic classes of minutiae which are identified as follows:

The *island, dot,* or *point* is an isolated ridge, approximately circular in outline, and with only one sweat gland pore; see Figure 41(a).

The *independent,* or *short ridge,* contains from two to six sweat gland pores; see Figure 41(b).

Rudimentary, interstitial, or *secondary* lines (or ridges) are characterized by the absence of pores, and some of them lie at a lower level than fully-formed dermal ridges. On a print, they show up as narrow lines and are omitted during ridge counting; see Figure 41(c).

Figure 40   Ridge minutiae

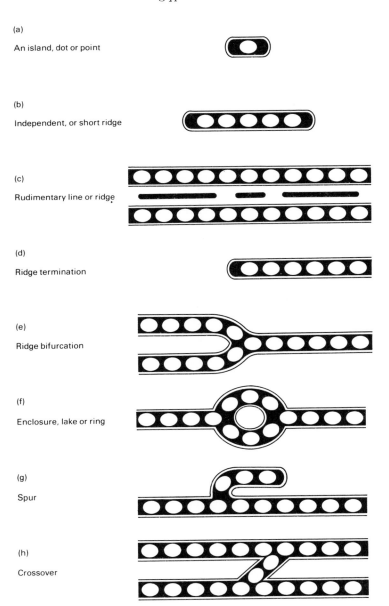

(a)

An island, dot or point

(b)

Independent, or short ridge

(c)

Rudimentary line or ridge

(d)

Ridge termination

(e)

Ridge bifurcation

(f)

Enclosure, lake or ring

(g)

Spur

(h)

Crossover

Figure 41   Eight classes of minutiae

Ridge termination, or *end* of ridge is self-explanatory; see Figure 41(d).

Branching, or *bifurcation* refers to a forking of the ridge pattern. It is sometimes known as a Y-formation; see Figure 41(e).

An *enclosure, lake*, or *ring* is a continuous ridge which outlines or surrounds a furrow. It could be described as two branchings in opposition on the same ridge; see Figure 41(f).

A *spur* is like a railway siding and resembles a lake formation, except that the ridge boundary is not completed; see Figure 41(g).

In a *crossover* formation two ridges are linked by a third short intersecting ridge; see Figure 41(h).

It's often difficult – if not impossible – to see the ridges clearly and distinctly with the naked eye, especially when the ridges are fine as they are in the hands of babies and children, and some women. Greater definition can be obtained by applying talcum powder to the hand, and then lightly brushing off all but a thin coating. A magnifying glass can be bought from any High Street optician and is invaluable for a detailed study of this sort, whether or not a print is being analysed; the difference with a glass is quite remarkable even with the lowest ratio of magnification.

In health, the sweeps and swirls of the papillary ridge patterns are unmistakable (see again the healthy example on p. 73). If the hands are continually in contact with chemical substances due to the peculiar nature of the subject's work, or are affected from within by biochemical changes of the kind that herald a breakdown in health they may be obscured to a greater or lesser degree by a cobweb of superfluous lines, or the ridge patterns themselves start to disintegrate. With the restoration of health, however, the original pattern always returns.

Investigations have been carried out into the possibility that crucial differences exist between the hands of male and female, negro, Caucasian, and other ethnic groups. Apart from the fact that females tend to have narrower ridges than males, in keeping with their, normally, smaller stature, and that the more complex pattern types are usually found in the hands of males, there seems to be no hard-and-fast rule. Racial differences in dermatoglyphic terms are also confined to tendencies. These might, in quite a large percentage, be due to in-breeding or endogamous practices leading to patterns being genetically transmitted and reinforced from one generation to the next.

Between 74 and 82 per cent of the homologous pairs of fingers in population samples of various ethnic groups have been found to bear the same fingertip pattern type.[21]

Dysplasia, hypoplasia, and *aplasia* are terms used to describe different degrees of imperfection in ridge development; usually a congenital condition resulting from disturbance during the period of ridge differentiation in the embryo. The severity of the irregularities depends on the stage of growth the embryo had reached when the disturbance occurred, and this gives the researcher important clues to the nature of the disruptive factor. A bit of detective work may show that the mother was, at that time, taking such-and-such a drug, or had been exposed to some sort of environmental pollutant.

Areas of aberrant ridge formation can vary tremendously from small patches to the entire surface of ridged skin on hands and feet. In some cases, the ridged skin is completely absent and the palms and soles present a peculiarly shiny appearance. *Total ridge aplasia* is a very rare phenomenon which seems to be genetically transmitted and is usually – though not always – connected with other abnormalities.

In *congenital ridge hypoplasia,* the ridges exist but aren't as well-developed as normal, healthy ridges. Because they are reduced in height, they don't come out as clearly in a print. An additional feature is often the excessive number of finely etched secondary creases which add considerably to the problems of dermatoglyphic analysis. A further difficulty is that ridge atrophy – which can accompany many illnesses, inherited or not, and appear at any stage of life – is impossible to distinguish from congenital ridge hypoplasia. However, if the disease can be successfully treated, the atrophied ridges can and will regenerate. Regular check prints are useful in such cases.

In *ridge dissociation* the ridge patterns start to break down until they no longer give the appearance of smoothly flowing continuous lines. In the early stages the printed pattern is still distinguishable but has a dotted appearance – an effect that has caused them to be referred to as 'strings of pearls' by workers of a more poetic turn of mind. Later, the design breaks down completely, until there is no way of telling what the original pattern was. Figure 42 shows the fingerprint of an individual with severe ridge dissociation. Some studies claim to have found a sequential relationship in this loss of pattern. In one of these the frequency of affected fingers was found to decrease in descending order, as follows: first the thumb, then the index, the ring, the middle, and the

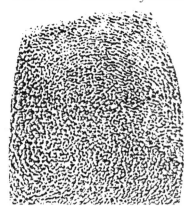

Figure 42   Abnormal fingerprint showing dissociation

little finger. In another study of apparently normal individuals the frequency was first, the middle finger, then the thumb and index, the ring finger, and the little finger. In the first study quoted, the sample was German, and in the second, Japanese. Once again the abnormality may be limited, or total, and transmitted via dominant genes, or associated with certain medical disorders including deaf-mutism and coeliac sprue. Other research workers have suggested a possible link between the state of the individual glands, the palms and finger tips, but a good deal more research is needed in this area before the theory can be adequately proven. Unfortunately, in spite of Penrose's attempts to regulate and standardize terminology and make it easy to recognize a particular feature or pattern from a verbal description if necessary, there is still a certain amount of confusion. Hypoplasia and ridge atrophy is all too often mentioned in a paper when the accompanying illustration shows a good example of ridge dissociation.

The work carried out by Noel Jaquin, Beryl Hutchinson, and the Society for the Study of Physiological Patterns, tends to support the theory of the hand as homunculus, with specific parts of the hand relating to specific areas of, and organs in, the body. Acupuncture, foot reflexology, and, in particular, iris diagnosis came into being as a result of exactly this sort of relationship. Unfortunately, they are considered too 'way out' for serious consideration and suffer the same sort of prejudice as hand analysis, yet a full (and scientifically approved) investigation into the laws behind such correspondences would, I feel, produce worthwhile results.

GEOGRAPHY OF THE RIDGE PATTERNS

Areas where the ridges form roughly parallel lines, when they appear straight, or very nearly so, are known as *open fields* and often referred to by the capital letter 'O'. As Penrose points out, the use of this term is 'sometimes extended to cover all fields which do not contain configurations considered to be significant by the investigator concerned'. Significant configurations can take a variety of forms, the most common of which are referred to as *fans, ladders, arches, whorls* or *loops*. It is uncommon for more than 20 p⟨ cent of the palmar or plantar ridged surface to be patterned – most of it is made up of open fields.

With rare exceptions, the finger tip patterns fall into one of three basic categories: loops, arches, and whorls. Pattern variants can usually be included in a sub-heading under one or other of these. Figure 43 shows some examples of classic types. Nature can spring weird and wonderful combinations of these on the unwary investigator. Having made it his business to try and make sense out of the ridge patterns he has to find a

Figure 43   Examples of loops, arches and a whorl

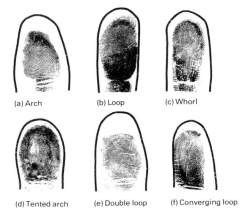

(a) Arch   (b) Loop   (c) Whorl

(d) Tented arch   (e) Double loop   (f) Converging loop

method of analysis and comparison which can successfully be applied to any formation.

The simplest pattern of all is the arch, see Figure 43(a), which is made up of a gentle sweep of ridges, uncomplicated by *apices* or *triradii*. This is known as a *plain* (or simple) arch, and other examples of it may be higher or lower. On the finger tips the pattern always follows the curve of the tips. Because the accepted system of *ridge counting* depends on there being one or more triradii in existence we have the somewhat ridiculous situation in which arches, *tented arches* and some low-lying loops are assessed as having a zero ridge count.

It seems that in dermatoglyphics, ridge counts, *total finger ridge counts*, and *absolute finger ridge counts* (TFRC and AFRC respectively) don't mean what they imply at all:

Ridge counting is used to indicate the pattern size. It is primarily utilized on fingertips and toes as a way of expressing the difference between digital triradii or the ridge density in a given area.

And the

TFRC expresses the size of a pattern, whereas the AFRC reflects the pattern size as well as the pattern intensity, which depends on the pattern type.[21]

I'm sure there must be an easier, more straightforward way of doing it but the experts obviously know best!

The tented arch has a core and therefore a triradius (the point at which three ridges meet, or diverge). It is therefore a 'true' pattern, unlike the simple arch, which in a technical sense is not. In a tented arch, it is usual for the distal radiant to point vertically towards the tip of the finger. The ridges pass over this as canvas would a tent pole, hence the name, see Figure 43(d).

The most common pattern in the Western hemisphere is the loop. There are two types: one coming from the thumb side of the hand, known as a *radial* loop, the other coming from the outer or percussion edge, and known as an *ulnar* loop. Each loop has one triradius, located on the point opposite the loop opening, see Figure 43(b). Loops may be short or tall, large or small, and relatively simple structures or more complex, see Figure 43(e) and (f).

The definition of a whorl, according to Galton, was a system of ridges with two or more than two triradii, one on either side of the pattern. In practice, this can be confusing, and Henry (1937) updated the police identification procedures by limiting the expression to those configurations which actually possessed a central core, see Figure 43(c). Most dermatoglyphic workers continue to follow the Galtonian classification. This gives us *simple* whorls of the type just noted (*concentric* whorl is another name for the same type), *spiral* whorls, in which the ridges eddy round the core in a clockwise, or counter-clockwise direction. Some whorls combine circles and ellipses, or circles and spirals, and the pattern size is variable. *Central pocket* whorls are patterns in which a small whorl is enclosed within a loop, see Figure 43(e) to (f). Like loops, these are classed as ulnar or radial, depending on which side the loop opens.

Yet another type of pattern is termed a whorl by the dermatoglyphicist, and a loop by the scientific hand analyst. The *lateral pocket*, and the *twinned loop* whorl, each possess two triradii, the accepted mark of the whorl, and it is this factor which has led to the confusion. Patterns which can't be fitted into any of the above categories are known as *accidentals* (rather a strange way of putting it, at least from the palmist's viewpoint: if one pattern is 'accidental', then surely *all* are!). This

Figure 44   Actual prints (a) are displayed above schematic drawings with boldly traced type lines (b). A, a simple arch; B, a tented arch; C and D, loops (ulnar or radial); E, a simple whorl: F, a central pocket whorl; G, a double loop whorl; H, an accidental whorl

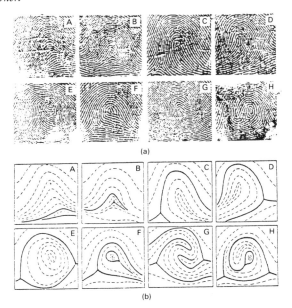

applies to any combination of two or more configurations, for example, a loop and whorl, triple loops and any other unusual formation.

Patterns also occur on the other two finger phalanges but compared to the finger tips, little attention has been paid to these areas. In many cases, the patterns here are obscured by secondary, crease, or 'stress' lines running vertically up the fingers. The few studies that have been carried out definitely suggest a strong hereditary basis for pattern transmission. The patterns found on the phalanges are normally much less complex than they are on the finger tips.

The dermatoglyphic formula relies on first defining, and then locating (on a standard diagrammatic representation of palm or sole), the patterns, in order that their type and relative intensity can be studied. The second part of the formula involves the ridge count system we've just glanced at. It's certainly not for the beginner! The *main lines* – nothing at all to do with the lines of traditional palmistry – are also indicated. Figure 45a is a typical representation of a hand as it looks after analysis. Figure 45b gives maps showing the dermatoglyphic geography of the sole of the foot.

Figure 45a

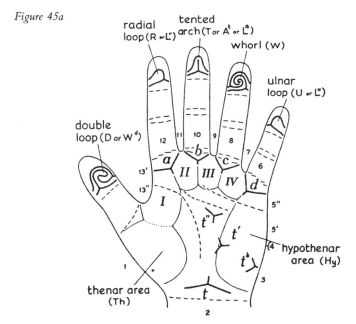

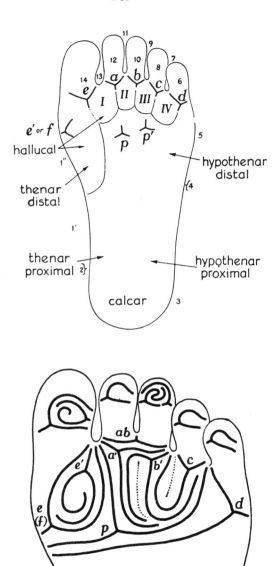

Figure 45b

The area immediately beneath the *hallux*, or big toe, is much longer than the comparable area on the palm. For ease of identification, it is therefore divided into two sections: *thenar distal* and *thenar proximal*. The same applies to the other side of the foot, where the sections are referred to as the *hypothenar distal* and the *hypothenar proximal*. The interdigital sections, as in the palmar map, are designated I–IV. The heel of the foot is referred to as the *calcar* area.

Soleprints are more difficult to take than palmprints. This is due not only to the fact that the ridging extends quite a way beyond the actual base of the foot in the majority of cases, but also to the problems involved in getting complete toe prints – toes aren't so easy to roll as fingers! Ill-fitting shoes also play their part. It's surprising to see just how many feet are malformed by years of imprisonment in fashionable footwear.

Similar configurations are found on both palms and soles, namely arches, loops, whorls and open fields, though on the feet the patterns tend to take on a more elongated form in keeping with the shape of the plantar surface. Loops are classified as being *fibular, tibial, distal* or *proximal* according to the initial, rather than the final, exit direction of their cores to avoid any confusion that might be caused by their convolutions. Open fields rather than true patterns, which are rare, are characteristic of the calcar area.

Apart from the difficulties that have to be overcome before a reasonable footprint is secured, many investigators feel that it isn't worth while. In their opinion, much more information can be obtained from the palm which *is* easily accessible. Without a great deal more research, it's impossible to confirm or deny that the plantar ridge patterns also hold medically significant data, but preliminary studies suggest that ridge breakdown in the palms may anticipate similar breakdown in the soles by several weeks. Perhaps the hand analyst should broaden his approach and add the examination of feet to his services – it would certainly set him apart from the crystal-gazers!

Standardizing nomenclature – dermatoglyphic or any other ·– invariably has two effects. First and foremost, the chances of accidentally and unnecessarily duplicating research are considerably reduced for meaningful discussion of ideas and current projects becomes possible, even likely. But only within a limited field. By the creation of an exclusive jargon, that field becomes more and more conservative, and resistant to change. Its unfathomable complexity ensures that fresh and unbiased insights are rarely, if ever, applied and a balanced overview of the work as a whole becomes impossible, or at best extremely difficult. Here we have yet another esoteric and occult doctrine in the making!

Dermatoglyphics is a science that deserves the attention of a wider audience, hence my attempts to strip away some of the mystique that has grown up around it. We know that, given the right tools, the human organism automatically seeks to repair itself, starting at cell level. My own work as a hand analyst has proved to me that this is so, for inevitably as part of the healing process the tell-tale signs in palms and soles disappear, leaving a clear, untroubled surface. If the body is equipped with its very own early warning system, and is able to indicate – often many years in advance – tendencies towards specific weaknesses and diseases, surely more people should be aware of it?

High-tech diagnostics are all very well, and we're right to marvel at the cleverness of the minds that are able to design such equipment as EEG machines, scanners, dialysis apparatus, pacemakers, sophisticated body function monitors and the rest. How wrong, though, to ignore the possibility – and it's a strong one – that the human body itself may have a built-in system of analysis and diagnosis, providing a print-out, quite literally, at its finger tips! But what exactly have dermatoglyphicists achieved to date? And why do scientific hand analysts feel that more could, and should be done? In the next two chapters we'll discuss these questions and their widespread ramifications as fully as possible.

9

Dermatoglyphics Today

   . . . the physicist proclaims aloud that the physical phenomena which meet us by the way have their forms not less beautiful and scarce less varied than those which move us to admiration among living things. The waves of the sea, the little ripples on the shore, the sweeping curve of the sandy bay between the headlands, the outline of the hills, the shape of the clouds, all these are so many riddles of form, so many problems of morphology, and all of them the physicist can more or less read and adequately solve: solving them by reference to their antecedent phenomena, in the material system of mechanical forces to which they belong, and to which we interpret them as being due.

   . . . Nor is it otherwise with the material form of living things. Cell and tissue, shell and bone, leaf and flower, are so many portions of matter, and it is in obedience to the laws of physics that their particles have been moved, moulded and conformed.

D'Arcy Thompson, On Growth and Form[20]

The examination and analysis of many hundreds and thousands of prints, worldwide, has led to the recognition and acceptance by dermatoglyphic experts of a norm. Patterns that don't match up to that accepted norm are classed as deviant, and here once again, we're brought face to face with the fundamental dichotomy between the dermatoglyphicist's approach to hand analysis and that of the scientific palmist. But an artificial framework of this nature has inbuilt limitations, as we've already noted.

The dermatoglyphicist seeks similarities, automatically rejecting as abnormal anything that falls obviously outside these contrived parameters – yet there is nothing more unnatural or unlikely in real life than actually meeting up with such a standard or average example. The hand analyst has his types, but uses them only as convenient pegs on which to hang his findings. He accepts an individual's differences for what they are – normal and to be expected, and broadens his knowledge by studying them carefully.

Because so many exceptions to their rule were noted, and 'because of the inherent variability of skin-ridge configurations' some early dermatoglyphicists became disillusioned. They had hoped that inspection of the skin ridges – in accordance, of course, with the rigid and unbendable laws they had themselves laid down – would provide infallible indications of specific chromosomal defects. Clinicians had been led to expect that this new science would enable them eventually to draw conclusions from particular ridge formations, much as they had been used to doing from more orthodox symptoms. Some, indeed, are still working from within these narrow boundaries.

If dermatoglyphics as a science is to fulfil any of its early promise, I think we have to adopt a fresh and more open-minded stance. We must remain objective, but try at the same time not to limit our expectations. There are still potent and substantial reasons for believing that an organized study of the palmar and plantar dermatoglyphs has far more to offer researchers than confirmation of the existence of genetic defects and chromosomal disorders. Of course that doesn't mean throwing out what has already been discovered: there's still much to interest and stimulate the serious medical investigator. It may mean taking a fresh perspective. Gathering and sifting through the data collected, not only by dermatoglyphicists, but also by psycho chirologists and hand analysts, is likely to be extremely productive. Nuggets confirming the existence of many rich seams, ripe for mining, will otherwise be missed.

It's rather ironic that, back in 1943, in the preface to *Fingerprints, Palms and Soles*, Harold Cummins and Charles Midlo expressed almost identical sentiments:

Perhaps because the publications of research are scattered, and the generalizations seemingly hidden in complexities of descriptive method, it is not generally appreciated that the patternings of epidermal ridges on fingers, palms, toes and soles have broader and more fundamental significance.

Cummins and Midlo, however, were complaining of the lack of interest in dermatoglyphics due to the belief that the palmar patterns had 'no importance beyond their use in personal identification.' The two American Professors of Anatomy successfully opened up the field and made it a respectable science to study. Since that time anthropologists, anatomists, zoologists, geneticists, and even general practitioners have taken an interest in this specialized branch of human biology.

Cummins and Midlo gave some attention in the penultimate chapter of their classic work to the possibility that the skin-ridge patterns might reveal a subject's susceptibility to disease, and in particular inherited disease.

If such distinctions exist they are of the utmost moment in analysis of the constitution of disease, because they demonstrate that susceptibility to the disease, like the distinctions in dermatoglyphics with which it is correlated, is inborn.[5]

The first delvings into this possibility were made at the end of the nineteenth and beginning of the twentieth centuries when general interest in fingerprint patterns was at its height. It was no coincidence that in 1901 Scotland Yard adopted the Edward Henry system of fingerprint identification, giving it a worldwide boost.

These pioneer workers claimed to have found distinctive statistical trends. Unfortunately, their enthusiasm wasn't matched by efficient methods of investigation, and inadequate samples and limited controls didn't help them to prove their case to the sceptics. On the contrary, their results worked against them. They were too anxious to claim success for their hypothesis and neglected to record important substantiating details, such as sex, age, race, and the known state of health of their subjects.

An exception to this, shown in Figure 46 in table form, sets out to investigate the comparative frequency of whorls and arches in the various forms of schizophrenia. Although the statistical difference isn't conclusive it certainly seems as though the Germans, the Danes, and the East Prussians are racially more prone to whorled fingertips than most other Europeans, including the English, who show a greater tendency to loop patterns. Our propensity towards loops has been confirmed many times. Since those early studies, instigated in the 1930s, many more have been carried out. According to the chief of pathology at St Luke's Hospital, Utica, New York State, it is now possible to diagnose, with close to 90 per cent accuracy, schizophrenia and leukaemia. Dr Stowens feels that dermatoglyphic techniques have much to offer as a diagnostic aid, and also in determining which individuals are at risk of developing diabetes or cancer in later life. Links with other illnesses are being investigated.

The link between specific dermatoglyphic peculiarities and Down's syndrome is well known, even to district nurses and midwives. Another

FREQUENCIES OF WHORLS AND ARCHES IN THREE INDEPENDENT SERIES OF SCHIZOPHRENICS, COMPARED WITH CONTROLS FROM THE GENERAL POPULATIONS

	Germans (Poll)				East Prussians* (Duis) Schizophrenics		Danes (Møller)			
	Control		Schizophrenics		Schizophrenics		Control		Schizophrenics	
	(845) Male	(776) Female	(232) Male	(545) Female	(416) Male	(356) Female	(86654) Male	(14857) Female	(450) Male	(583) Female
Whorls......	33.6%	26.8%	28.5%	28.1%	30.2%	29.6%	29.8%	25.3%	27.0%	26.2%
Arches......	4.3	7.6	5.7	6.6	5.2	7.8	5.4	7.5	7.7	8.2

* The geneaology of all these subjects was traced at least as far as through their grandparents, and East Prussian origin of each generation was established. In the absence of a control, it should be explained that the higher whorl frequencies, as compared with Poll's material, are the expected associate of more frequent whorls in the general population of this territory.

Figure 46

syndrome with characteristic dermatoglyphs is thalidomide-triggered teratogenesis. Epidermal ridge patterns are grossly distorted in direct proportion to the damaged limbs of the victims. Ridge dissociation is common, and palmar creases abnormal. A predominant feature is the tendency to a single transverse crease. The line that normally bounds the thumb was often reduced in size.

Missing, extra, or otherwise abnormal thumbs or digits are usually associated with abnormal to grossly abnormal ridge and finger tip patterns. The common link appears to be that internal and external physical abnormalities and aberrant dermal ridge patterns are genetically determined, with damaged genetic material being either inherited or affected environmentally at the embryonal stage. Whether inherited patterns are due to recessive or dominant genes is a question that continues to tax the experts, but the fact that they can be inherited is generally accepted.

Distortions of ridge arrangement in these cases are secondary effects of abnormal gene action, the primary effects being developmental disturbances in the foetus.[27]

In *anonychia*, an inherited condition in which finger- and toe-nails are absent or vestigial (usually missing on index and middle fingers, less often on the thumb, and much reduced on the ring finger), ridging continued over the area that would normally have been covered by the nails. In some cases, ridge patterns extend to the middle phalanges of the fingers instead of being completed on the tip. This only applied when nail and nail bed were absent. Another, similar condition, also inherited, is known as the *nail patella syndrome* but here the nail bed is present and, though the ridged skin still encroaches on the area normally occupied by the nail, the pattern distortions are less distinctive.

The fingernails of his patients have long been a fruitful source of information to the observant doctor. Blueness of the nails, especially obvious round the moons, can lead to a diagnosis of cyanosis – acutely deficient oxygenation of the blood. Accompanied by clubbing of the finger tips, heart disease would be suspected. Nail anomalies are common in endocrine disorders and mental deficiency. Normally the nails are among the first tissues to develop in the growing foetus making their appearance as early as the ninth week after conception. The keratinous construction of nail and hair is similar and the nails, like the hair, lose their smooth shininess when vitality fails. Their rate of growth slows, too, as a result of prolonged ill health.

Other signs of past or present adverse health conditions are horizontal or vertical ridging of the nail. General debility and poor diet can lead to furrowed nails – in particular, deficiencies in vitamins A, B complex, and D. Such deficiency may be the result of prolonged mental stress, or eating denatured, processed foods. White spots on the nails have been variously ascribed to poor calcium metabolism, zinc or magnesium deficiency, and/or B6 deficiency. (The B vitamins should *never* be taken singly, as this will induce deficiencies of the B vitamins *not* supplied.)

Pituitary and thyroid disturbances have a definite effect on the nails. Under-activity of the thyroid is reflected in brittle, slow-growing, dull-looking nails. Occasionally, they are soft, rather than brittle, and fan-shaped. Short, striated, moonless nails are symptomatic of hypo-pituitarism. Extremely rapid growth may be a sign of glandular over-activity. In mental deficiency, whether or not genetically induced, there is a tendency for atrophied, misshapen, moonless nails.

Henri Mangin-Balthazard's book, *La Valeur Clinique des Ongles*, published in 1932, is one of a very small number of works devoted to the study of the nails. Interestingly, his findings tend to support the clinical and psychological meanings traditionally assigned to the nails by chirologists:

M. Mangin confirms the physical basis for the empirical belief; the glandular system being, in its turn, associated with health and temperament. The tradition of temper and health indications being assigned to the nails is therefore borne out and may be considered reliable as far as it goes.[12]

The Diseases of the Nails by Pardo-Castello, published in 1936, is a more specialist and detailed work which also makes the connection between glandular disturbance – especially the thyroid and pituitary – and nail distrophy. As in hand analysis generally, there are conflicting views about the value of the nails as an aid to diagnosis and prognosis and much more research needs to be done in this area.

An interesting experiment correlating nail morphology with ence-phalograph readings was carried out at the Maudsley Hospital, London, in the 1950s. Dr Doust, carrying out a programme of research into the patterns of blood vessels under the nail, discovered that in babies and young children the capillaries normally take the form of straight, or nearly straight, lines. These are gradually translated into attenuated arch patterns bearing a strong resemblance to long, open-ended hairpins. The process is generally completed by the age of eight years. Dr Doust dis-covered that in the mentally immature, and those inclined to give way to basic emotions, such as rage, the patterns were imperfectly developed, manifesting as low arches. In the truly neurotic, he found that the long form had begun to develop but with a twist in it. Dr Doust's findings were apparently checked against brain wave tests, and a correspondence demonstrated. The implication here is that character and personality may be much more closely linked to our physiological and chemical status than has previously been allowed. Foods are known to have a direct effect on the brain, and it is anticipated that in the not-too-distant future cer-tain of the amino acids will be prescribed for such diverse conditions as depression, insomnia, and pain relief. It seems the old saying, 'you are what you eat', may not be so far out after all!

Other inherited abnormalities accompanied by dermatoglyphic distor-tion include *zygodactyly*, or webbing of the fingers and toes (see again Figure 25b); actual fusing of some of the bones of hand or foot, or both, a condition that may be accompanied by such gross distortion that print-ing is impossible; *apical dystrophy*, in which the finger tips are missing at birth, with the exception of the thumbs which, though abnormally formed, are usually complete with nail: and *polydactyly*, where there are extra fingers or toes. All these conditions are comparatively rare, though you may come across an individual who has had a minor op to remove a supernumerary digit, or unsightly webbing between his fingers. The expert would find clues to the aberration in the ridge patterning of the palm, most often at the distal border.

Chromosomal and single-gene defects have provided a vast field for dermatoglyphic investigation, the surface of which has only been scratched. Abnormalities may be found in any of the twenty-two pairs of autosomes or the two sex chromosomes, leading to some degree of deformity. Such abnormalities seem always to be associated with irregularities of the dermal ridges of palms and soles. Particularly gross physical and dermatoglyphic anomalies are found when there are extra, or missing chromosomes.

Trisomy is the term used when a chromosome, normally one of a homologous pair, is present in triplicate, that is when the extra chromosome is indistinguishable from a pair in the normal complement.[27]

A well-known autosomal trisomy is Down's syndrome, or trisomy 21, accounting for up to 94 per cent of all patients with Down's. In the remaining 6 per cent either translocation of chromosome 21, or a degree of mosaicism of the same chromosome has taken place, an abnormality more fully described in Chapter 6.

Trisomy of one of the chromosomes in groups 13 to 15, or D (there are seven groups) is referred to as *trisomy 13* for convenience, though in reality, because their size is so similar, it's hard to know exactly which chromosome is involved. Another name for the same syndrome is *large acrocentric trisomy*. As the symptoms are so extreme, most cases survive only a few weeks and therefore there is a paucity of dermatoglyphic records, though Penrose observed a significant increase of patterns on the ball of the thumb, and between the middle and ring fingers. As in mongolism, there is a preponderance of single transverse lines and only one crease on the little finger. Patterns on the soles of the feet are less frequent than normal. Extra and vestigial digits are common, and mental retardation, cleft palate, deformed eyes and ears, hare lip, and heart weakness characteristic.

Trisomy 18 (or *17*) is characterized by an elongated skull, heart defects, mental retardation, malformed ears and kidneys, and a single umbilical artery. Few babies survive their first month, though modern technology keeps about ten in every hundred cases alive to one year. As far as the hands are concerned flexion deformities are common: the fingers remain permanently flexed, with only one crease. Though there is no significant increase in the arches of relatives compared to controls, simple arches seem to predominate in the patients themselves. In patients diagnosed as suffering the full trisomy 18, arches are reported in over 90 per cent of all finger tip patterns. Indeed, more than 40 per cent possessed the full set of ten digital arches. On palms and soles pattern intensity was much reduced. The single transverse crease was noted, in one study, in 75.5 per cent of the cases observed.

Trisomy 8 mosaicism has been less well studied than the three previous trisomic conditions, but some strikingly similar dermatoglyphic traits have already been noted. Deeper than normal crease lines on palms and soles, nail abnormalities, simian lines, greater frequency of finger tip arch patterns, high palmar and plantar pattern intensity, and low TFRC (total finger ridge count) are characteristic. Clinical manifestations of the syndrome are psycho-motor retardation, prominent forehead, deformed nose, heart and kidney defects, skeletal abnormalities such as absent patellae and/or extra ribs and vertebrae, and a tendency to frequent chest infections. Dermatoglyphic data on this condition is still being collected from patients and their families, but a clear profile for trisomy 8 mosaicism has already emerged.

At present, the science of genetics is itself far from precise. This lack of precision represents a bar, not only to accuracy in linking an apparent syndrome with a specific chromosomal aberration, but also to possible dermatoglyphic identification of that syndrome as an isolated patho-logical condition in its own right. However, rapid technological advances suggest that it won't be long before the expert is able, unerringly, to point out the individual chromosome causing the trouble by its proportions and position in the cell nucleus. When that happens, positive dermatoglyphic labelling of chromosomal aberrations will become a feasible proposition, and accepted as valuable corroborative evidence in diagnosis.

The sex chromosomes, X and Y, are similar in size to groups C and G respectively of the autosomal complement, and are relatively easy to identify. Sex chromosome abnormalities don't have quite as much effect on ridge formation as autosomal defects. There does seem to be a definite relationship between the number and type of sex chromosomes and the total finger ridge count, and for ridge breadth to increase in direct ratio to the number of additional sex chromosomes. A study by Penrose and Loesch (1969) confirmed that multiple X chromosomes had less effect on ridge breadth than multiple Ys did. Sex chromosome abnormalities that have been and are being subjected to dermatoglyphic analysis include Turner's syndrome which results in women of small stature, with underdeveloped breasts and immature development generally (including lack of menstruation and subsequent infertility), and Klinefelter's syndrome which affects males only.

Klinefelter's varies between patients having just the one additional X chromosome, thus giving a chromosomal complement of 47, instead of the normal 46, and extra X and/or Y chromosomes up to a total of 49. In other cases (46, XX Klinefelter syndrome) the number of chromosomes is normal but the male may suffer from underdeveloped testes, penis and scrotum, and he lacks facial hair. According to Schaumann and Alter, pooled data on this form of the syndrome revealed little out of the ordinary in the way of dermatoglyphic data except that the ridge breadth on the subject's finger tips corresponded more closely with the mean for normal females than males.

The most common form of Klinefelter's syndrome exhibits two X chromosomes and a Y. In such cases, intelligence is usually normal – but mental retardation becomes more prevalent in direct ratio to the number of supernumerary chromosomes involved. Clinically apparent features of the syndrome don't develop till adolescence and skeletal abnormalities such as deformed elbow joints are typical. Extreme tallness, long hands and feet and abnormalities of the little fingers are also characteristic. Dermatoglyphic features on palms and soles haven't been found to deviate significantly from normal, though some researchers consider there to be a lower pattern intensity on the soles of the feet of patients with the syndrome, compared to controls. A slight increase in finger tip arch patterns, and a lower total finger ridge count was noted by others.

Dermatoglyphic analyses have also been made of the palms and soles of patients suffering structural chromosomal aberrations. In the quaintly named *cri-du-chat* syndrome, characterized by the high-pitched, cat-like mewing of the babies and children born with it, it is chromosome 5 which is abnormal. In one major study, victims with a mixture of some normal and some abnormal chromosomes (mosaicism), or chromosomal aberrations other than deletion of part of the short arm of chromosome 5 were omitted. In the cases that remained a particular setting of the fourth interdigital loop pattern was observed in over 75 per cent, and a single transverse palmar 'crease' line in over 80 per cent. Partial webbing of the young patients' fingers and toes was also common. Even in those cases where no webbing was found, a tendency to syndactyly was suspected. Warburton and Miller (1967) suggested that fusion of the triradii at the bases of the middle and ring fingers might provide a clue to such a tendency which had, for some reason, not been realized in the embryo.

In patients with Wolf-Hirschhorn syndrome (where it is the short arm of chromosome number 4 which is 'deleted', or broken off), the cat-like cry characteristic of *cri-du-chat* syndrome is not present, but many of the other clinical symptoms are. Foot deformities are common, as is cleft palate. Dermatoglyphic analysis suggests increased frequency of arch patterns, particularly in males, and a decrease in whorls, compared to controls. A single transverse palmar flexion crease is also common, being found in over half the cases analysed. Pattern frequency on the ball of the thumb was increased, while hypothenar patterns were less frequent than normal. Most striking of all was the discovery of ridge dissociation in 81 per cent of the cases reported, varying in extent between small areas and the entire ridged surface area of hands and feet. In controls, including most medical disorders, such ridge dissociation is rare.

Dermatoglyphic signatures seem to be more distinctive in those individuals suffering marked deformity of hands and feet than those whose limbs are relatively normal. Single gene disorders and disorders in which the mode of genetic transmission is still uncertain have also provided research workers with data. The De Lange syndrome, like many already discussed, is characterized by increased frequency of thenar patterns and single transverse palmar crease lines. Ridge dissociation is common, as are loop patterns on the palm, and radial loops on the finger tips. In the Rubenstein-Taybi syndrome, large and complex patterns on the ball of the thumb – rare in normals – were found in over half the cases examined. Complex patterns occurred on many of the patients' thumbs and big toes, far more frequently than in control groups. Taken overall, it seems that, whatever the syndrome, certain features tend to recur providing non-specific indications of abnormalities. The single transverse palmar crease and increased frequency of finger tip arch patterns, for instance, are extremely common.

Some research workers feel that dermatoglyphics should be used as a tool, not merely for identifying chromosomal abnormalities, but for genetic counselling. Dermatoglyphic analysis of would-be parents is painless, risk-free, and inexpensive to boot, unlike many of the techniques currently in use. A German scientist, Professor Rodewald, of the Saar University, Homburg, has been collecting data on both patients and their parents in the hope of gaining a better understanding of the factors producing the genetic and dermatoglyphic aberrations, and, in particular, the possibility of forecasting the risk of transmitting damaged chromosomes by examining parental ridge patterns.

Rodewald and his colleagues have found that unusual combinations in the dermal ridges of palms, soles and finger tips do appear with exaggerated frequency in the parents of Down's syndrome affected children.

A definite relationship was established between abnormal dermatogly-phics and the parent responsible for the transmission of the supernume-rary chromosome 21. In forty out of ninety couples, this was subse-quently verified by the application of standard cytogenic tests. Similar investigations are being made with the cooperation of parents of children suffering from other syndromes.

Though most research programmes have devoted their resources to analysing the link between chromosomal/dermatoglyphic anomalies, ill-nesses in which the genetic influence, if any, isn't so obvious have also been investigated. As far as congenital heart disease is concerned, pub-lished results are contradictory with some sources claiming to have found diagnostically useful dermatoglyphic features, and others refuting these claims on the grounds that the quality of much of the work is 'abysmal'. Paediatrician Dr T.J. David, of Manchester University, England, feels that not enough care has been taken in the past. His review of previous studies 'revealed major technical deficiencies'. All too often, for example, the sample is too small, given the naturally occurring variations between the print patterns of normal people. This leads inevitably to serious errors and inconsistencies, especially as some researchers exa-mined only the palms, others the fingerprints, and yet others only one palm. Statistical analysis of the various results was also found wanting in many respects.

In Dr David's view, much more care needs to be taken at the outset to choose patients who are similarly afflicted and accurately diagnosed. Sex and age are important considerations, and care should be taken to ensure that, apart from the disease being studied, the control group represents a similar cross section of sex, age and class. There is obviously a need for some sort of standardization of procedure here, if dermatoglyphics is to achieve the scientific acclaim it deserves, with each research paper detail-ing methods and results fully so that the study could, if required, be repeated in order to confirm and amplify those results.

An important investigation by Dr David into the connection between. dermal and epidermal ridge atrophy and coeliac sprue substantiates the authors' findings, namely that nutritional deficiency – indeed any con-dition resulting in malabsorption of vital nutrients, has an immediate effect on the condition of the skin ridges. Summing up his findings in the second of two reports (1970 and 1973), Dr David concludes, 'It is sug-gested that finding epidermal ridge atrophy in an adult should alert the physician to the possibility of coeliac sprue.' The breakdown of the skin ridges in coeliac disease was found to occur in 90 per cent of adults studied over a continuous four-year period. Ridge atrophy receded when the patients were put on a gluten-free diet but the improvement was rarely a complete return to normal. Steroid treatment, in addition to a gluten-free diet, seems to lead to a marked, but temporary, improvement in the ridge condition, suggesting that stress overload, and adrenal exhaustion, have a part to play in the development of this disease – as indeed they do in very many other common ailments. Unfortunately, long-term use of steroid medications is now known to have some pretty drastic side-effects and is contraindicated in all but the most extreme cases (see *Medicines*, by Professor Peter Parish, Penguin Reference Books).

More recently, a report by a group of Indian researchers into a possible association between dermatoglyphs and duodenal ulceration was published in the *Journal of Human Heredity* (volume 32, 1982, p. 432). Results of previous family, twin, and blood group studies suggested that a genetic factor might be at work in the development of such ulcers. Ninety adult males suffering from duodenal ulcers were palm-printed, and their dermatoglyphic features compared with those of sixty-four healthy males. Habibullah and his colleagues reported a significant increase in the frequency of whorls and a reduction in that of loops, and increased pattern frequency between the ring and little finger bases and on the upper ball of the thumb, compared to the control group.

It's rather ironic that the *New Scientist* and *The Times* should have used this as a bandwagon on which to jump, in order yet again to knock the palmist! Noel Jaquin, Beryl Hutchinson, and other non-fortune-telling hand analysts have been making the connection between types of finger tip pattern and susceptibility to particular types of disease for years. When whorls predominate, the individual seems to have difficulty expressing himself, he tends to 'bottle up' his feelings rather more than most, and to be dogmatic and a mite inflexible. In short, the sort of person you'd expect to suffer from ulcers and digestive disturbances. Loops, on the other hand, reflect a more adaptable, versatile personality who is emotionally vulnerable and prone to nervous exhaustion and possible breakdown. In both instances of course, these susceptibilities would have to be confirmed by referring to other features in the palms, such as the angle and condition of the Head and Life lines.

Diet and environmental pollution, though important causatory factors in disease, don't provide the full story. Our personalities and the way we cope, and our individual chemical reactions to stress are vital. One man's 'upper' is another's 'downer' so to speak and we're beginning to discover that the same applies to the pharmacists' 'magic bullets' that were to have cured all our ills.

Iatrogenic, or medicine-exacerbated, disease continues to cause concern, and the National Health Service to degenerate into an 'illness' service with a very small percentage of its resources being ploughed into preventive medicine, or research into the causes of ill health, as opposed to manufacturing a drug-bullet for each and every symptom. Financing such an exercise is like trying to fill a bottomless bucket. In 1977, total expenditure in Britain on medical research alone exceeded £100 million, while the projected budget for a single trial on hypertension was more than £1 million.

Dermatoglyphics, and other research projects having no marketable end-product totter along on a pittance: a stark contrast to such largesse. In this country, research programmes are financed by four types of agency. Government agencies and university laboratories are funded, directly or indirectly, by the taxpayer. Charities – like the Cancer Research Campaign – are funded by voluntary public subscription. The drug companies, hardly the most disinterested of sponsors, plough back a large percentage of their profits into research – and promotion – of new wonder drugs. Vast conglomerates like ICI, Fisons, Roche and Bayer are hardly likely to back the sort of programme that could, in the long-term, put them out of business. Healthy people don't need drugs, so they're not going to be too keen on furthering the cause of preventive medicine.

Whatever the reason, the support that has been given to dermatoglyphic research workers here in Britain is derisory. The few existing projects are under-financed and sadly under-manned, while in other more emotive areas such as cancer research, work is all too often duplicated. Frequently, newly qualified doctors anxious to make a name for themselves channel their ambition into researching promising – one might even say fashionable – techniques and 'cures'. Organ transplants, and the development of anti-rejection drugs are currently high on this list as is genetic engineering, all of which, of course, involve experiments on animals. Inevitably, valuable time, effort, and resources are wasted.

In *Paper Doctors*, Vernon Coleman, himself a GP, describes the *Index Medicus*, a monthly publication which is:

two inches thick, has 1000 pages and contains nothing at all but the titles of medical research papers published throughout the world. In one . . . issue . . . there were no fewer than seventy-five papers dealing with potassium – papers such as 'A study of the calcium, potassium and sodium content of toad atria' . . .

A conservative estimate is that 20 per cent of research work is unintentionally repeated by other workers.[33]

Dermatoglyphic research isn't immune from this sort of unnecessary duplication and, so far, it has concentrated mainly on trying to identify specific diseases from palmar and plantar ridge formations. An essential stage, but once sufficient confirmation has accumulated to prove that these signals *can* be relied on to foreshadow a tendency towards a particular type of breakdown, researchers should surely change direction. An attempt must be made to instigate preventative measures, if at all possible. Papering over the cracks, making do and mending, is no longer enough. Knocking out symptoms with magic bullets, even if there were no risk of side-effects, doesn't get anywhere near the real cause, whatever that might be. And heartwarming demonstrations of public sympathy and amazing generosity, as orchestrated by the TV programme *That's Life* in 1984 for little Ben Hardwick, are made all the more poignant when you realize that only a small proportion of the money invested in organ transplantation would go a long way towards discovering *why* our livers, kidneys, hearts and lungs are failing with ever-increasing frequency. But organ transplants are more dramatic, they're good box office. Marvellous for selling newspapers and getting a programme to the top of the ratings! Mere prevention isn't nearly as exciting.

Christian Barnard filled the massive football stadium in Rio twice when he talked of how he performed the world's first heart transplant, yet the majority of his audience could not afford the simple medicine to rid themselves of their intestinal worms.[35]

The healthy scepticism which greeted research findings a mere half century ago has been replaced by a child-like, unreasoning credulity in a public which has been conditioned by the media to believe that doctors and medical scientists have, or are about to make a breakthrough which can't fail to produce spectacular cures for all our ills. These men are, as Ian Kennedy so aptly puts it, the 'new magicians', but magicians ill-equipped by their training to know exactly what a healthy person is. There's little enough time after all to learn about the symptoms of disease! Modern medicine 'is concerned with reaction, response to ills which already ail the sufferer [instead of] inquiring into the causes and origins of illness with a view to preventing them.'

A minority is starting to question the results obtained by orthodox practitioners and seeking alternatives which try to stimulate the natural healing mechanisms of the body. An article in the *Nursing Times* on the subject of iatrogenically induced illness reminds us that a mere third of the world's total population,

has access to western-style medicine, and that the rest rely entirely on acupuncture, homeopathy, ayurdic medicine, unani, herbalism, naturopathy and various forms of spiritual and psychic healing.

There is no doubt that technology and computer science have an important part to play in discovering why, in some people, the symptoms of imbalance manifest as a cancer, and in others as arthritis, or multiple sclerosis, asthma, emphysema or a number of degenerative diseases. The old moulds are being broken. Transformation and innovation are in the air, but this time the drive and impetus is originating in patients who are disillusioned with the mechanistic approach to healing. There is encouraging evidence to suggest that their numbers are being swelled by doctors, and a recent headline in a national newspaper actually suggested that fringe medicine might be on the way to winning a 'seal of approval' from the British Medical Association. According to the *Daily Mail*, 17 August 1983, that august and conservative body 'is launching an inquiry into all forms of alternative medicine – and some may become available on the Health Service'.

Whether or not the BMA approves the 'alternatives' that approximately two-thirds of the world regards as absolutely normal, the face of medicine as we know it today is changing. People are less and less satisfied to be merely free from diagnosable illness. They are seeking to attain that elusive degree of vibrant health and well-being that goes with childhood, and which is every man's birthright – and his, rather than the doctor's – responsibility. 'That productive, satisfying, joyful health which results when an individual is balanced and integrated in body, mind and spirit'. An unmistakable feeling of 'wellness' that shines forth as limitless positive energy and is invariably reflected in the condition of palms and soles.

10

The Role of Hand Analysis in Healing and Health Care

I have often thought that one of the less attractive traits of various professional bodies and institutions is the deeply ingrained suspicion and outright hostility which can exist towards anything unorthodox or unconventional. I suppose it is inevitable that something which is different should arouse strong feelings on the part of the majority whose conventional wisdom is being challenged or, in a more social sense, whose way of life and customs are being insulted by something rather alien.

I suppose, too, that human nature is such that we are frequently prevented from seeing that what is taken for today's unorthodoxy is probably going to be tomorrow's convention. Perhaps we just have to accept it is God's will that the unorthodox individual is doomed to years of frustration, ridicule and failure in order to act out his role in the scheme of things, until his day arrives and mankind is ready to receive his message . . .

HRH Prince Charles[36]

After nearly sixty years the study of dermatoglyphics is just starting to become respectable. References are appearing in the occasional medical encyclopedia here and there – a sure sign that it's teetering on the edge of general scientific acceptance, even if this is, at present, limited to its role in the genetic field. Since 1926, when Cummins and Midlo first named this specialist study of the skin ridges, progress has been steady, but painfully slow. A combination of factors, as we've seen, was responsible for this. First and foremost, the unsavoury occult connection with palmistry and fortune-telling, and secondly, the Establishment's well-known habit of crucifying the original thinker before he has a chance to upset the comfortable certainty, the order and stability, represented by the well-entrenched status quo. The length of time taken for any new idea to breach the defences of conservatism, and gain the acceptance of, in this case, the orthodox medical profession is legendary, varying between decades and centuries.

Hand analysis as a science in its own right, quite apart from dermatoglyphics, is gradually throwing off its fortune-telling image. It is proving an invaluable tool in assessing physical and psychological wellbeing at each end of the spectrum and has been used to great advantage in fields as diverse as careers guidance, marriage and compatibility counselling, health monitoring, and child guidance. There need be no mystery or mystique about it: with a working knowledge of scientific palmistry each of us is potentially able to know himself, his family and friends, effectively stripping away the masks most of us are so used to wearing we've forgotten they're there. The masks behind which we imagine we're invulnerable, but which in reality separate us from the rest of humanity, leaving us, all too often, isolated and alone. And anything that cuts us off, either from other people, or from our environment, will sooner or later lead to mental, physical, social or spiritual malaise.

The trained scientific hand analyst can assess an individual's character and health potential only because the same laws apply to us all. A feature has the same basic implication no matter whose hand it is found in. Like any other science, scientific palmistry is firmly based on empirically testable facts. This being so, it follows that anyone who is truly interested and possessed of the necessary self-discipline can learn to read hands for his own and others' benefit. The rational approach to palmistry is, like the good doctor's diagnosis, based on minute and painstaking examination. Not only the lines, but the shape, texture, temperature and colour of the hands and the ridge and furrow patterns of palm and fingers are taken into account.

The scientific palmist learns from experience that the hand appears to map its owner's life,

character and physique; it tells of his character and potentialities in its shape; of his inherited tendencies in the pattern of the skin where also may be found indications of health conditions long before the factual appearance of illness in the body. The blueprint to the electrical circuits may be seen there as the outward picture of the nervous system; and the brain's cognizance of its impulses. The lines also record the memories and experiences that have been strongly felt.[15]

As we know, palm-reading has intrigued and titillated both the mystery schools and the masses from the very earliest times – Man has a deep-seated need to identify his place in the infinite scheme of things.

Reference to the lines and signs in his palms is made several times in the Bible, and in the secret doctrines of faiths a good deal more ancient than Christianity.

The reputable palmist, one working from a scientific rather than an intuitive base, doesn't pretend to be able to 'lift the veil' and peer into the future. He *is* sometimes prepared to take a calculated guess about the consequences of continuing along a particular path in life. The fact that he is able to do this isn't as unlikely as it sounds. Body chemistry and emotional responses are controlled by the brain – the limbic system was proved by scientists in the late 1970s to be the part of the brain specifically linked with strong emotions. And our characteristic emotional responses dictate our individual pattern of action and reaction, not only to other people and the environment in general but also to more specific stresses and stimulants, such as drugs. Hence the old saying about one man's meat being another's poison.

A drug is essentially any substance – and that includes herbs – able to exert a measurable effect on our metabolism and body chemistry. Hand analysis helps to determine the effect such substances are having on us, and whether they are affecting our physical, mental, or spiritual balance for good or ill. A beneficial therapeutic programme is soon reflected in improvement in the condition of the skin ridges, and of course in the condition of the patient; an invaluable aid for future doctors.

Many depressives have come to me for help, guidance, and reassurance and though a large proportion nursed a secret dread of insanity, more than 90 per cent proved to be suffering not mental, but biochemic breakdown. Poor diet, denatured, over-refined and processed foods on top of 'normal' daily stresses had proved the last straw, and sub-clinical vitamin deficiencies were all too common. Sodium/potassium balances were often upset, leading to pre-menstrual tension, weepiness, and in extreme cases suicidal tendencies. Magnesium/B6 deficiency was also implicated, especially in those eating white, rather than wholemeal, bread, and living on a diet with next to no fibre.

Symptoms varied, depending on the element required and the individual's biochemic requirement but all too often my client was lacking vitality and motivation, couldn't cope with everyday life, felt alienated from family and friends, and could find nothing to look forward to. All without exception had consulted their family doctor. Most had been prescribed Librium or Valium or other tranquillizers, and many had been referred to psychiatrists with negative results. Neither group – doctors nor psychiatrists – had any knowledge of the valuable work being done by Dr Richard Mackarness in the field of food allergy and mental illness. His two important books were written for the consumption of the general public – medical colleagues scoffed, and are still scoffing, at the idea that food allergies can be responsible for such an incredible diversity of mental and physical symptoms. It is now almost sixty years

since Rowe first used his elimination diets to prove that chronic ailments like migraine, dyspepsia, eczema and ulcerative colitis could be cleared up by elimi-nating wheat, eggs, milk and other common foods from patients' diets. Rowe and others . . . have shown that the elimination of milk and milk products can cure at least one case in five of ulcerative colitis, a crippling disease of the large bowel which can lead to cancer.[37]

Other symptoms that may be allergy linked are panic attacks, chronic anxiety, hyperactivity and violence (frequently seen in children allergic to sweets and chocolates), delusions, hallucinations, itchy rashes that come and go, swelling of the hands or lips, arthritis, various aches and pains, cramps, tachycardia (racing pulse, often accompanied by dizzi-ness), catarrh, hay-fever, mouth and peptic ulcers, asthma, cystitis, impotence, frigidity, and menstrual disorders.

Some kinds of schizophrenia are now believed to be symptoms – in the form of an allergic response – rather than illnesses in their own right. Richard Mackarness describes research carried out in America in the 1960s by F. Curtis Dohan, a doctor working at the hospital of the Uni-versity of Pennsylvania. Dr Dohan had noted a drop in the incidence of schizophrenia in occupied countries during the Second World War. As soon as food became more readily available, however, reported cases rose to equal the previous norm: between 0.85 and 1.2 per cent of the popu-lation. Dr Dohan divided one of his wards into two groups,

restricting cereals in one group, and giving the ordinary hospital diet, rich in starch, to the other. Drugs were withheld from both groups so as not to obscure the issue. Before long, a change in the behaviour of one group became apparent: the patients on the no-cereal diet were more approachable, their thoughts were less disordered, and some who had never left the ward were able to go out to work or to go home. The other group remained as deluded and hallucinated and psychotic as ever.[37]

Many researchers have noted a connection between stress overload and allergic reaction. The eminent physiologist, Hans Selye's work on stress spans more than half a century and he concludes that such reactions are often no more than the body's response to overload. Adelle Davis, the American nutritionalist, believed that adrenal exhaustion invariably preceded allergic symptoms. She pointed out that,

Such stresses as inadequate diet, emotional upsets, insufficient sleep, infections, or the use of drugs usually precede the onset of allergies . . . Healthy cells can prevent harmful substances from entering them. A lack of almost any nutrient, however, increases cell permeability, as if a fine sieve were replaced by a coarse one; therefore valuable nutrients can leak from such cells and toxic materials pass into them.[38]

The finger tips are closely linked with the glandular system and any malfunction shows itself in vertical lines. In severe cases these make it difficult to see the patterns on the tips. In adrenal exhaustion, the length of the fingers, and the palms are covered by a mass of superficial lines which often obscure the ridges completely.

Once this stage is reached, regaining equilibrium – mental or physical – becomes a problem. Like a set of dominoes that is set to fall in rapid sequence, once the initial impetus is provided there's little time to lose. And even if the process is stopped before total and complete collapse occurs, a lot of time and effort are required to re-establish homeostasis.

The human body incorporates so many fail-safe devices that we take its stability for granted, forgetting that this happy state is achieved and maintained by the very finest adjustments to internal and external stimuli. As Professor Pichet observed in 1900, 'In a sense it is stable only because it is modifiable – the slightest instability is the necessary condition for the true stability of the organism.'

The earliest signs that all is not well appear in the hand long before orthodox symptoms are visible. Breakdown of the ridge patterns – the 'dissociation' of the dermatoglyphicist – in specific areas of the palm has been connected by some hand analysts, notably Beryl Hutchinson, with mineral imbalance. Mineral imbalance in its turn is implicated in the chain of biochemic reactions leading to disease. The sodium/potassium balance is vital to cell health. Too much sodium (and sodium is added to an amazing number of processed foods) can upset this balance. In some individuals, this leads to an inability to think clearly, in others blood pressure or the heart rhythm may be affected. In the hand, chaining or islanding of Head and Heart line gives the hand analyst a clue to these conditions.

Copper deficiency (unusual in the British Isles – an overdose is far more likely) is seen in the fading of the lines, which according to Beryl

Hutchinson 'look as though they had been rubbed out with an india-rubber'. Copper is essential for the functioning of the nervous system, helps convert iron to haemoglobin, and is integral to certain digestive enzymes. Lack of this trace element can lead to anaemia, premature grey-ing of the hair, and heart problems. In one genetic disorder, transmitted by recessive genes, a fault in metabolism causes copper to accumulate, with fatal results, usually before the age of puberty.

The Society for the Study of Physiological Patterns has continued the work started by their late President Beryl Hutchinson MBE, into mineral imbalance and possible clues in the hand. So far, the evidence that has accumulated is impressive with over a dozen mineral deficiencies capable of identification from signs on palm, fingers, and nails, apart from the potassium and copper deficiencies already mentioned. Calcium fluoride, an essential component – not only of bones and tooth enamel, but also the elastic fibres of connective tissue and skin – signals its lack by the appearance of lines beneath the Heart line, under the ring and little finger. Gumboils, whitlows, and defective tooth enamel are more con-ventional symptoms of the deficiency.

Calcium phosphate helps to promote cell growth and coagulation of the blood. It is found in blood plasma and corpuscles, saliva, gastric juices, connective tissues, bones and teeth. If it is unable to be absorbed for any reason, or if an insufficient amount is assimilated, earache, tooth-ache, gastric problems, and rheumatism are common complaints. Defi-ciency shows itself in white spots on, and brittleness of, the fingernails. As yet there has been no definite link made between a lack of calcium phosphate and degeneration of lines or skin ridges.

Iodine is one of several vital nutrients used by the body in the manu-facture of thyroxin, a hormone produced by the thyroid gland. This hormone is responsible for the individual's rate of metabolism: when too little of it is synthesized he or she tends to be lethargic, easily tired, have cold extremities, and gain weight on few calories. Overactivity of the gland results in rapid weight loss, due to increased basal metabolic rate, hands are usually clammy, and there is a tendency for the patient to be hyperactive and over-emotional. Any disease that affects the functioning of the thyroid gland results in the appearance of vertical lines disfiguring the tip of the little finger. In extreme cases, these lines are so numerous that they actually obscure the ridge pattern. If surgery has taken place, the lines show little improvement, but if the condition can be corrected by dietary or other means they will gradually fade away. Vertical lines on any of the finger tips – with the exception of those that appear after a long soak in the tub! – warn of glandular disturbance to some degree. Horizontal lines on the tips indicate unresolved frustrations.

As Beryl Hutchinson says, 'The iron in a human body is said to be only enough for a six-inch nail but without that nail the body falls to pieces.' The trace element, molybdenum, is necessary before iron can be efficiently absorbed, and sufficient hydrochloric acid must be produced for it to pass through the intestinal walls into the blood. Refined flours, white breads, cereals and sugars decrease iron absorption by stimulating the flow of alkaline digestive juices, and by killing off the essential intestinal flora that inhabit the gut of the healthy individual. Manganese is another trace element thought to act as a catalyst in iron absorption.

Iron deficiency shows up in the hand as paleness of the lines and finger nails but, in many cases, an iron tonic is no answer. If vitamin B6 and/or magnesium are also missing the ingested iron is inefficiently metabolized and red blood cells continue to die, without being replaced. Vitamins C, E and folic acid (another of the B-complex group) are important in iron absorption, especially in those exposed to insecticides and environmental pollutants. Even mild deficiency of this mineral leads to chronic fatigue, shortness of breath, rapid pulse on exertion, and constant headaches.

Many scientists dispute the suggestion that *any* mineral or vitamin deficiency is possible in this 'enlightened' age, because they are found in so many foods. Others, perhaps more well-informed, such as Henry A. Schroeder, a world authority on pollution and mineral deficiency, are agreed that:

the mass production of food and its necessary refinement, processing and storage add subtle toxins to food and remove some essential factors. Although the average level of nutrition in the United States and in other civilized countries has never been higher, the population, especially older people, have many diseases caused directly or indirectly by food.[39]

Zinc, for example, was first identified as an essential nutrient in 1934. It wasn't till almost twenty years later that the possibility of a shortage in man was recognized. Since that time, researchers have been amassing evidence which proves conclusively that zinc deficiency is associated with such skin complaints as acne, dermatitis, and psoriasis. Joint pains, loss of appetite and the sense of smell, retarded sexual development, schizophrenia, and hyperactivity in children have all responded to zinc supplementation. As it is used in every cell in the body for the production of DNA and RNA, and in enzymes, a shortage of this mineral can be expected to have wide-ranging consequences, and it does.

Beryl Hutchinson and her fellow researchers at the SSPP found that zinc deficiency shows in the hand as a fine chaining of the Life line, starting halfway round the ball of the thumb. The keratinous structure of hair and fingernails is also affected. The hair may become brittle and start to lose its colour prematurely, and the nails become fragile and lacklustre. White flecks or banding of the nail is also common, but as the nail takes five to six months to grow out, this is not a good guide to a patient's current nutritional deficit of zinc.

The cell is of course the basic building block in the body, and any dietary imbalance will in some way affect the completed structure. How such imbalance weakens each of us in a different manner, triggering different symptoms, is a matter of conjecture, but it is known that we inherit not only gross physical defects genetically, but also less readily diagnosed metabolic defects. Our genes hold the blueprint for the manufacture of enzymes: enzymes programmed to build, and enzymes with instructions to demolish, conserve and recycle. Inefficient or sloppy directions undermine our potential for health, and this is reflected in breakdown of the skin ridges. Each cell is a stage, and every nutrient has a part to play on that stage. Many scenarios are known and understood by scientists – but there are many more mysterious happenings and 'actors', some apparently playing 'bit' parts, but others with major roles, whose significance is not yet fully appreciated.

Each single cell is as important as every other, for:

This cell with all its processes and activities, multiplied by billions and billions, is you. The degree to which this cell can maintain its ideal structure and can carry on its normal functions is the degree of your health. A seemingly minor lack of a single nutrient or of many nutrients can damage the structure and/or interfere with its functions; a severe deficiency of one or more nutrients can bring about disaster. It is the amount of nutrients supplied to the cell itself which determines the state of your health.[40]

The fashionable trend towards 'junk' and convenience foods has been gathering momentum since multi-national enterprises first muscled in on the industry in the early post-war years. Today more than 60 per cent of the average food budget is spent on processed items. Reading the labels of some of these can be a salutary experience! Even cottage cheese, described as 'natural', contains its share of preservatives. Processed foods contain significant amounts of colouring, flavouring, and preservatives, many of which are suspected of being hazardous to health. Tests are considered by many to be inadequate, and in any case take no account of the varying amounts each individual consumes, or their cumulative effect on his personal biochemistry.

Are such additives necessary? If food needs to be coloured, flavoured, and otherwise disguised to make it appear palatable surely we'd be better off without it! I can recall a fellow caravanner in Spain last year brandishing a British loaf that must have been at least six weeks old – pure, white and deadly – and boasting as she squeezed it enthusiastically, 'Look! It's still fresh!' For food manufacturers desperate to expand profits, it has made economic sense to develop synthetic flavours (bacon-, cheese-and-onion-, and ham-flavoured crisps, for instance). And if a product *has* to stand on a shelf somewhere for six or more months, it doesn't make economic sense to have it turn a slightly different colour. Some bright consumer might decide he prefers the item that looks fresh, and leave the others standing.

Every year a few more previously permitted food additives are suspected of undermining health. Allergies, in all their wide variety, and cancer, are just two of these conditions. Yet,

Between 2,500 and 3,000 chemical additives are now thought to be in common use in the food industry. Thus people are persuaded to buy food which is created in a factory rather than grown on a farm. This is good for the industry because it is much more profitable to sell an item of processed food which has 'value' added to it, than it is to sell the original product. It is a more attractive proposition to market a packet of potato chips than it is to sell the original potatoes at a much lower price, but these high profits are often maintained at the cost of the consumers' health.[34]

Little wonder I have so few healthy prints in my collection. Can it be altogether coincidence that those belong in the main to people enjoying a wholefood and/or vegetarian diet?

There are several encouraging signs, however, that times they are a'changing, and attitudes with them. Under the surface a revolution is brewing. The consumer, for the first time, is starting to become aware that he doesn't have to sit passively by and take just what he's given – he's in the position of power because he creates the demand for a particular product. He can dictate the terms. This revolution is manifesting itself on the supermarket shelves, in the form of canned foods and jams emblazoned with the words, 'No Colour', 'No Preservatives', and new labels on traditionally acceptable items telling us of their 'High-Fibre Content'.

An 'exclusive' in the popular press told us that, according to a Gallup opinion poll the previous twelve months had seen a 60 per cent increase in the number of vegetarians 'and thousands more are changing their diets each month' (The *Sun*, 10 April 1984). Showbiz personalities, politicians, and even, it is rumoured, the Prince and Princess of Wales when 'at home', are helping to dispel the cranky, nut-cutlet image vegetarians have suffered from till very recently. If, as seems likely, this trend continues to broaden and encompasses organically grown foods, too, the chemicalized food industry will have to rethink its strategies.

Much of the stress we suffer is needlessly self-imposed. We crave artificial stimulation of our emotions at the expense of our glandular system; a craving whose demands are supplied by video and television all too frequently. The toxic residues of negative emotions can't fail to result in auto-intoxication of mind or body, or both, and equilibrium is destroyed. But, like a spoilt and precocious child, man is totally absorbed in dismantling himself and the universe to see what makes it tick. He's blissfully ignorant of the fact that he doesn't know how to fit the pieces together again. That, at least, appeared to be the case until comparatively recently for the majority, many of whom seem to be addicted to adrenal 'highs'.

Man's ability to adapt to the demands of his environment guarantees his survival both as a species and as an individual – provided the demands placed on his adaptive mechanisms don't exceed certain limits. Stress, in moderation, leads to better integration and greater flexibility by triggering a measured response from the endocrine glands, nervous system and the intelligence. Stress overload – and remember even holidays, parties, wedding celebrations and other happy events all have their stress quotient to contribute – provides fertile soil in which the seeds of disease can proliferate.

When stress goes beyond a certain point – and that point is different in each of us – pathological changes start to occur. But gentle stress, like gentle exercise, can be *gradually* intensified in a programme designed to build up strength and resilience.

The adaptation of the individual to a physiological, intellectual, and moral discipline determines definite changes in the nervous system, the endocrine glands, and the mind. The organism acquires, in this way, a better integration, greater vigour, and more ability to overcome the difficulties and dangers of existence.[1]

Biochemistry has the potential to monitor these shifting balances at cell level but often the first detectable signs of illness are visible in the lines and skin ridges of the hands, long before more commonly acceptable symptoms appear elsewhere. In this way, the body can signal, sometimes many years in advance, not only specific ailments and the areas and organs most at risk, but also underlying deficiencies.

Repeated often enough, messages between brain and nerve endings cause definable patterns to appear, especially on palm, sole and face. Who hasn't looked at the lines on a person's face and judged them to be of a certain disposition – kindly or bad-tempered – on that basis alone? Because the hand has the lion's share of nerve endings in relation to those found elsewhere in the body it's logical to assume that lines and signs are where hand analysis proves its true value. Expert examination of a patient's prints can reveal the underlying causes of his illness – vitally necessary if a cure is to be effected. It's important to realize though that health depends upon the harmonious interaction of the individual – mind, body, and soul – with his environment. Anything that disturbs that relationship, interrupting the free flow of energies and the fragile balance between the two, will inevitably lead to sickness. Our passion for specialization has made us forget that the words 'health' and 'whole' (or hale) come from the same root.

Two people can display similar symptoms of ill-health yet both can be suffering from entirely different complaints. The same people can have the same complaint and yet both present entirely different symptoms; the pain of the indisposition can even be felt in different organs.[13]

And,

The hand gives a perfect picture of the whole, with its relative strengths and interactions. It gives that much needed 'individual' picture. Every discovery made over the last twenty or thirty years in both psychology and curative medicine has stressed the vital importance of this 'individual' assessment of bodily and mental balance.[2]

Any strong emotion, whether it's negative or positive, causes a measurable chemical reaction in the body. Pleasure may bring a flush to the cheeks, while terror can cause the blood to drain away. It is in response to such stimuli as envy, hatred, and fear oft repeated that organic changes are set in motion. As a result of constant stimulation of the nerve-endings semi-permanent marks appear, but if the underlying cause can be identified and remedied, they will fade away again.

The effects of constant, unremitting pressure over a long period of time are clearly seen in Figure 47. In this print the major lines are thick and congested, and the whole hand is obscured by an ominous cobweb of

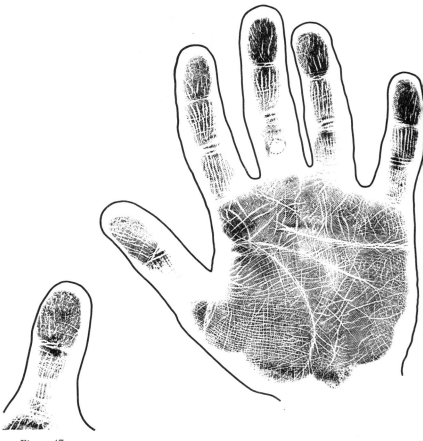

Figure 47

redundant lines. Even the skin-ridge patterns on the finger tips are gradually being obliterated. Accumulated stress had overtaxed the adaptive resources, and breakdown of some sort was imminent. Nine months later, after intensive psychoanalysis and nutritional changes to the patient's diet, the hands were much improved. The finger tips were almost clear, showing that the glandular system was recovering, and most of the superfluous lines had receded.

Jaquin presents a similar sequence in his book, *The Hand Speaks*. The prints of a 28-year-old man suffering from colitis and kidney infection were taken in the autumn of 1933, and again four years later when the infection had cleared (see Figures 48 and 49). It should be noted however that the latter is still not the print of a person who is 100 per cent healthy.

A more detailed account of the experiences of one of my own clients may be of interest here. June first came to see me in 1979. The print shown in Figure 50 was taken at that time, and she admitted that she had been on the verge of committing suicide. There seemed to be no solution to her problems and she was tired of fighting. This is a very messy print and even to the untutored eye the major lines are all unnaturally thick, frayed, or 'fluffy' in appearance.

After discussing the problems and June's lifestyle we agreed that it would be better for her to stop dissipating her vital energies in all directions, and to make a determined effort to channel them constructively into rebuilding her life. I advised June to take up a career in which she could use her talents to help others. She also admitted that she hadn't been watching her diet as carefully as she ought, and agreed to cut out the 'junk' foods she'd been indulging in. It was obvious that the hidden salts in the canned and processed food she'd been eating were having an adverse effect, possibly even triggering the depressive phases and the inertia.

Just over two and a half years later, June came to see me again, a much more positive and fulfilled woman. This time (Figure 51) the lines are finer and clearer, and the palm has broadened, showing that she had begun to develop some of her previously dormant gifts. She had cut out all added sodium, boosted her intake of fresh fruit and vegetables and was learning yoga and meditation. Though she still had the same problems as she'd had before, her attitude to them had changed. Now she was able to take them in her stride without faltering.

There is still a fair amount of stress shown in the vertical lines on the fingers, and the centres of the palms are still a bit messy, but all in all, the improvement is remarkable. It will be noted that the tip of the right little finger has *not* cleared. June had had part of her thyroid gland removed about six years earlier and the tip of the little finger is believed to mirror the condition of this gland. June's print adds some weight to this theory.

According to Beryl Hutchinson,

Many prints show the connection of the Little finger with the Thyroid Gland. We cannot yet prove whether it is under or overworking as both extremes show little lines rising from the joint and eventually covering the whole finger print, so that one can no longer be certain of the ridge pattern.[12]

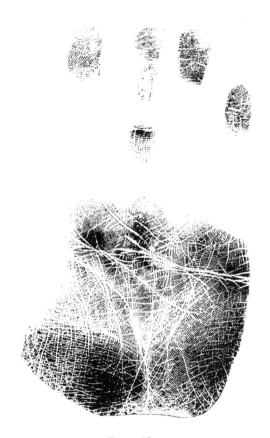

Figure 48

Figure 48   A case of colitis described in Noel Jaquin's book, The Hand Speaks[2].
This is his diagnosis:

Man aged 28. Single. Was suffering from colitis, and a bacterial infection of the kidneys and intestine. Imprints taken in autumn 1933.
Analysis. The fingers are definitely analytical. The will-power is strong, and the numerous lines of the hand show a high degree of nerve energy, as they are not only numerous but deep. The Head line has a frayed appearance, tending to split about an inch and a quarter along its length. It then continues as a normal line, but is definitely fluffed.
The wide space between Head and Life lines shows impatience and impetuosity, a basically restless disposition, which the general lining obviously accentuates. A high degree of nervous energy enables him to indulge in his desire for change and activity.

Figure 49

Faulty functioning of the kidneys indicated by the longitudinal line running down the outer cushion on the palmar surface below the little finger.
The malformed skin ridges are typical of intestinal bacterial infection, while the thick groups of malformations on the base of the cushion near the wrist indicate an intestinal catarrh, also of bacterial origin

Figure 49   *Jaquin analysed the hand again four years later, in 1937:*

The infections have been eliminated, and the functional deficiencies corrected. Note that the cushion is now quite clear. Also the lines are clearer, and even the incipient split in the Head line just below the third finger has mended slightly

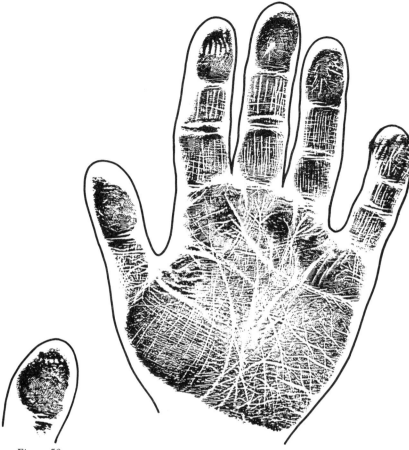

Figure 50

The investigations of the SSPP point to specific areas on the palm being linked with various parts of the body, but members are agreed that much more research needs to be done before their findings can be regarded as in any way conclusive. There is no doubting the fact that true health cannot come about in a vacuum, and neither the body, nor the palm, can start to become healthy until we realize that it's a state of being we can't achieve in isolation. Health is entirely dependent on harmonious interaction of the total man – mind, body, and spirit – with the environment.

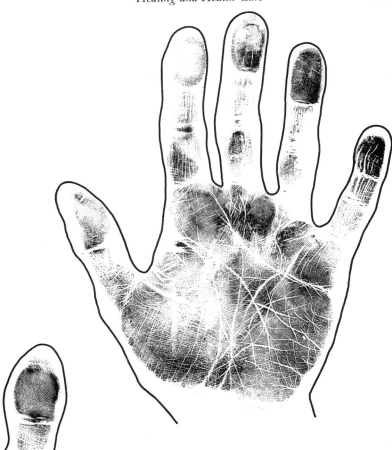

Figure 51

Whatever disturbs that relationship or interrupts the free flow of energies between the two, upsets a balance that is fragile at best and leads, sooner or later, to disease. Ironically, we habitually refer to those who live in a symbiotic relationship with nature and the elements as primitive. Yet their seasonal rites and rituals do little more than demonstrate an inherent and instinctive respect and reverence for our Mother, Earth.

Civilized man has stressed control of the elements to such a degree that he has nearly obliterated this relationship, and is consequently dangerously close to obliterating himself. We are beginning to understand that we are in no way apart from, or superior to, nature. Everything is linked, every part is interdependent, every organism and thing has a function and is meaningful to the whole. We cannot mistreat any part of nature without suffering the consequences. If we are to heal the violence we have already done to our environment, and if we are to understand the ways in which our environment can heal us, we must return to a loving relationship with nature.[25]

There are as many different definitions of health as there are therapies to cure illness. A general doctor will probably describe it as the relative absence of disease symptoms. In acupuncture, health exists when positive and negative energies – yin and yang – are perfectly balanced and flowing freely through and around the meridians. An osteopath or chiropractor will tell you health can only exist in the absence of osteopathic lesions. Health to a geneticist, or a biochemist is synonymous with cell health and stability, whereas to the psychiatrist mental health has as its fulcrum the ability to initiate and sustain fulfilling and meaningful relationships. And a priest or pastor might assess the spiritual well-being of his flock in terms of their ability to love God and their neighbours without breaking the ten commandments too often!

True health combines all these elements. Mental, physical, and spiritual health are closely linked and a weakness in any one area invariably affects the integrity of the whole – not necessarily in a negative way. Physical weakness often leads to a compensatory strengthening in another area. Helen Keller and many victims of the thalidomide tragedy are shining examples of what can be done by the physically handicapped, provided the mental attitude is right. Mother Teresa of Calcutta couldn't by any stretch of the imagination be described as robust, but no one could doubt her spiritual strength and integrity. I'm sure that if I were fortunate enough to be able to take Mother Teresa's handprints they would show a measure of fulfilment that is lacking in most people today.

After centuries of analyzing the process of sickness and disease from innumerable specialist angles (like the blind men with their elephant), the wheel has turned full circle. We are starting to realize that, after all, man isn't like a clock that can be taken apart and reassembled or a car with faulty parts which can be renewed to make it as good as new. Man is a 'familiar and profoundly mysterious entity' and

neither the soul nor the body can be investigated separately. We observe . . . a complex being, whose activities have been arbitrarily divided into physiological and mental.[1]

Physical disease may have 'psychosomatic' elements, emotional responses may be triggered by food allergy, and feelings in their turn trigger a physiological, neuro-endocrine response. But the mind itself is undeniably the most important single factor in the development of disease. I'm sure we can all remember at least one occasion when we felt under the weather, and sudden good news or an emergency requiring our immediate attention drove all thoughts of illness away. Thoughts are powerful enough to put a drain on our vitality, or increase it. 'Whatever the mind can conceive and believe, the mind can achieve' is an affirmation that can be applied to every aspect of life. Recent research has proved that the value of the placebo lies in the patient's belief in the remedy. His faith that it will work causes the brain to release endorphins into the blood stream, thereby stimulating the healing potential of the body itself.

It is that same brain that initiates a never-ending dialogue between the nervous system and the palms of the hands, and causes minute alterations in the lines and condition of the skin ridges. We have attempted, in this book, to demonstrate the relationship between the hand, the brain, and our health status.

I have been convinced, through my own limited researches into the hand and health, that it is possible to diagnose with incredible accuracy the current and future fitness of any individual. And, most important of all, that it is possible to detect abnormalities in time to instigate preventative measures well before symptoms appear in the rest of the body.[6]

Sources

See the Bibliography for further information on some of the following publications.

1. Alexis Carrel, *Man the Unknown*, Hamish Hamilton, 1935
2. Noel Jaquin, *The Hand Speaks*, Lyndoe and Fisher, 1942
3. Charlotte Wolff, *The Human Hand*
4. Fred Gettings, *The Book of the Hand*, Hamlyn, 1965
5. Harold Cummins and Charles Midlo, *Fingerprints, Palms and Soles*
6. David Brandon-Jones, *Practical Palmistry*
7. Francis Galton, *Finger Prints*
8. William G. Benham, *Laws of Scientific Hand Reading*
9. Anika Bergson and Vladimir Tuchack, *Zone Therapy*, Pinnacle Books (New York), 1974
10. Julius Spier, *The Hands of Children*, Routledge and Kegan Paul, 1955
11. Anthony Masters, *Mind Map*, Eyre Methuen, 1980
12. Beryl Hutchinson, *Your Life in Your Hands*
13. Noel Jaquin, *The Hand of Man*, Faber & Faber, 1933
14. Frederic Wood-Jones, *The Principles of Anatomy as Seen in the Hand*
15. Beryl Hutchinson, *A Handbook on Hands*
16. A. Glazewski, an article in *Radio Perception*, September, 1951
17. John Napier, *Hands*
18. W. Ritchie Russell and A.J. Dewar, *Explaining the Brain*, Oxford University Press, 1975
19. Aubrey Milunsky, *Know Your Genes*, Pelican, 1980
20. D'A.W. Thompson, *On Growth and Form*, Cambridge University Press, 1961
21. Blanka Schaumann and Milton Alter, *Dermatoglyphics in Medical Disorders*, Springer-Verlag (New York), 1976
22. Thomas Verny (with John Kelly), *The Secret Life of the Unborn Child*
23. Geraldine Lux Flanagan, *The First Nine Months of Life*, Heinemann Medical Books, 1970
24. Taken from *Touch the Earth*, and quoted in Cristina Ismael's *The Healing Environment*

25. Cristina Ismael, *The Healing Environment*
26. Taken from C.G. Jung's introduction to Julius Spier's *The Hands of Children*
27. Sarah B. Holt, *The Genetics of Dermal Ridges*, Charles C. Thomas (Illinois, USA), 1968
28. Jack Lucas, *Our Polluted Food*
29. Taken from the works of Herbert Spencer (1820–1903), philosopher and individualist
30. Lyall Watson, *Lifetide*, Coronet Books, 1980
31. Richard Dryden, *Before Birth*, Heinemann Educational Books, 1978
32. Peter Watson, *Twins*, Hutchinson and Company, 1981
33. Vernon Coleman, *Paper Doctors*
34. Lesley Doyal, *Picture of Health*, Broadcasting Support Services – Channel 4
35. Ian Kennedy, *The Unmasking of Medicine*
36. HRH Prince Charles, speaking to the British Medical Association on the occasion of its 150th anniversary
37. Richard Mackarness, *Not All in the Mind*
38. Adelle Davis, *Let's Get Well*
39. Henry A. Schroeder, *The Trace Elements and Man*, The Devin-Adair Company, 1973
40. Adelle Davis, *Let's Eat Right to Keep Fit*

Bibliography

PALMISTRY & HAND ANALYSIS

Benham, William G. *The Laws of Scientific Hand Reading*. Hawthorn Press (New York), 1946.

Brandon-Jones, David. *Practical Palmistry*. Rider, 1981.

Cummins and Midlo, *Fingerprints, Palms and Soles*. Dover Publications (New York), 1943.

Galton, Francis. *Finger Prints*. Da Capo Press (New York), 1965.

Hutchinson, Beryl. *A Handbook on Hands*. Rider, 1953; *Your Life in Your Hands*. Neville Spearman, 1967.

Napier, John. *Hands*. George Allen & Unwin, 1980.

Scheimann, Dr Eugene. *A Doctor's Guide to Better Health through Palmistry*. M.D. Parker (USA), 1969.

Wood-Jones, Professor Frederic. *The Principles of Anatomy as Seen in the Hand*. Baillière Tindall, 1949.

Wolff, Charlotte. *The Human Hand*. Methuen, 1942.

HEALTH, HEALING AND THE MEDICAL ESTABLISHMENT

Arehart-Treichel, Joan. *Biotypes*. W.H. Allen, 1981.

Coleman, Dr Vernon. *Paper Doctors*. Temple Smith, 1977.

Davies, Dr Hywel. *Modern Medicine – A Doctor's Dissent*. Abelard-Schumann, 1977.

Davis, Adelle. *Let's Get Well* and *Let's Eat Right to Keep Fit*. Unwin Paperbacks, © Harcourt, Brace & World, 1965.

Dytchwald, Ken. *Bodymind*. Wildwood House, 1978.

Gaer-Luce, Gay. *Bodytime*. Temple Smith, 1971.

Glasser, Dr Ronald J. *The Body is the Hero*. Collins, 1977.

Hackett, Earle. *Blood, the Paramount Humour*. Jonathan Cape, 1973.

Illich, Ivan. *Limits to Medicine*. Pelican, 1977.

Ismael, Cristina. *The Healing Environment*. Celestial Arts, 1973

Kennedy, Ian. *The Unmasking of Medicine*. George Allen & Unwin, 1981.

Kidman, Brenda. *A Gentle Way with Cancer*. Century, 1983.

Mackarness, Dr Richard. *Not All in the Mind* and *Chemical Victims.* Pan, 1976.
Parish, Professor Peter. *Medicines – A Guide for Everybody.* Penguin, 1979.

BOOKS OF RELATED INTEREST

Alder, Vera Stanley. *Wisdom in Practice.* Rider, 1970; *When Humanity Comes of Age.* Rider, 1972; *The Fifth Dimension.* Rider, 1983.
Bucke, R M. *Cosmic Consciousness.* E.P. Dutton & Co, 1901.
Carson, Rachel. *Silent Spring.* Penguin, 1982.
Chaitow, Leon. *Relaxation & Meditation Techniques.* Thorsons Press, 1984.
Cooke, Grace. *Meditation.* The White Eagle Publishing Trust, 1965.
Gotzsche, Anne-Lise. *The Fluoride Question.* Davis-Poynter, 1975.
Hamblin, Henry Thomas. *Within You is the Power* (14th ed. 1983) and *The Power of Thought* (11th ed. 1982). The Science of Thought Press, Bosham House, Chichester, Sussex.
Lucas, Jack. *Our Polluted Food.* Charles Knight & Co, 1975.
Roberts, Jane. *The Nature of Personal Reality.* Prentice-Hall, 1974.
Verny, Dr Thomas (with John Kelly). *The Secret Life of the Unborn Child.* Sphere Books, 1981.

MONTHLY MAGAZINE ON HEALTHY LIVING

Here's Health.

Anyone interested in following up the ideas expressed in this book should contact:

The Society for the Study of Physiological Patterns,
39, Larchwood House,
Baywood Square,
Chigwell, IG7 4AY,
Essex.

Acknowledgements

The authors and publishers would like to thank the following for permission to use illustrations:

Baillière Tindall Ltd (from *The Principles of Anatomy as Seen in the Hand* by Frederic Wood-Jones, 1949) figs 18, 19, 23

J. N. Barron figs 25a, 25b

Charles C. Thomas, Publisher, Illinois, USA (from *The Genetics of Dermal Ridges* by Sarah B. Holt, 1968) fig 35

Dover Publications Inc (from *Fingerprints, Palms and Soles: An introduction to dermatoglyphics* by Harold Cummins and Charles Midlo, 1943) figs 40, 46

Fingerprint Whorld fig 30b

Hamlyn Publishing Group Ltd (from *The Human Body* by Paul Lewis and David Rubenstein, 1970) fig 22

Her Majesty's Stationery Office (from *The Finger Print System at Scotland Yard* by Frederick R. Cherrill, 1954) fig 34

International Institute of Reflexology, Harlow, Essex fig 6

John Napier figs 9, 10, 11, 12, 15, 16

The National Foundation (from *Memorandum on Dermatoglyphic Nomenclature* by L.S. Penrose – March of Dimes, New York, IV(3), 1968) figs 30, 39, 45a, 45b

Neville Spearman Ltd (from *Your Life in Your Hands: A modern guide to palmistry* by Beryl Hutchinson, 1967) fig 24

The Williams & Wilkins Co, Baltimore (from *Medicine* 46:35 1966, 'Dermatoglyphic Analysis as a Diagnostic Tool' by M. Alter) fig 44

Index